Power Maths

Year 6
Practice Book 6B

White Rose Math

> Draw your favourite animal.
>
> What do you think its mass is in kg?

This book belongs to _____ .

My class is _____ .

Series editor: Tony Staneff Lead author: Josh Lury

Consultants (first edition): Professor Liu Jian and Professor Zhang Dan

Author team (first edition): Tony Staneff, Josh Lury, David Board, Catherine Casey, Belle Cottingham, Neil Jarrett, Timothy Weal, Paul Wrangles and Zhu Dejiang

Pearson

Contents

Unit 7 – Ratio and proportion   **6**
Use ratio language   6
Introduce the ratio symbol   9
Use ratio   12
Scale drawing   15
Scale factors   18
Similar shapes   21
Ratio problems   24
Problem solving – ratio and proportion (1)   27
Problem solving – ratio and proportion (2)   30
End of unit check   33

Unit 8 – Algebra   **35**
Find a rule – one step   35
Find a rule – two steps   38
Form expressions   41
Substitution (1)   44
Substitution (2)   47
Formulae   50
Form and solve equations   53
Solve one-step equations   56
Solve two-step equations   59
Find pairs of values   62
Solve problems with two unknowns   65
End of unit check   68

Unit 9 – Decimals   **71**
Place value to 3 decimal places   71
Round decimals   74
Add and subtract decimals   77
Multiply by 10, 100 and 1,000   80
Divide by 10, 100 and 1,000   83
Multiply decimals by integers   86
Divide decimals by integers   89

This looks like a good challenge!

Fractions to decimals   92
Fractions as division   95
End of unit check   98

Unit 10 – Percentages   **100**
Understand percentages   100
Fractions to percentages   103
Equivalent fractions, decimals and percentages   106
Order fractions, decimals and percentages   109
Simple percentage of an amount   112
Percentage of an amount – 1%   115
Percentages of an amount   118
Percentages (missing values)   121
End of unit check   124

Unit 11 – Measure – perimeter, area and volume   **126**
Shapes – same area   126
Area and perimeter   129
Area and perimeter – missing lengths   132
Area of a triangle – counting squares   135
Area of a right-angled triangle   138
Area of any triangle   141
Area of a parallelogram   144
Problem solving – area   147
Problem solving – perimeter   150
Volume – count cubes   153
Volume of a cuboid   156
End of unit check   159

My power points   162

It is time to do some practice.

How to use this book

Do you remember how to use this **Practice Book**?

Use the **Textbook** first to learn how to solve this type of problem.

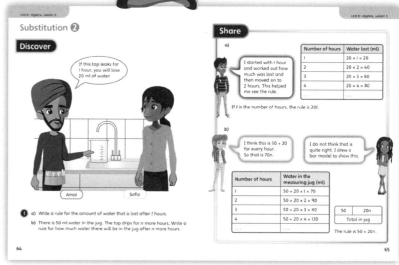

This shows you which **Textbook** page you need.

Have a go at questions by yourself using this **Practice Book**. Use what you have learnt.

CHALLENGE Challenge questions make you think hard!

 Questions with this light bulb make you think differently.

Reflect

Each lesson ends with a **Reflect** question so you can think about what you have learnt.

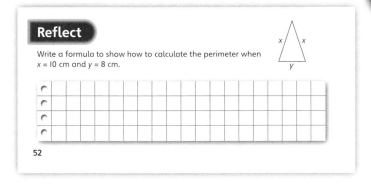

Use **My power points** at the back of this book to keep track of what you have learnt.

My journal

At the end of a unit your teacher will ask you to fill in **My journal**.

This will help you show how much you can do now that you have finished the unit.

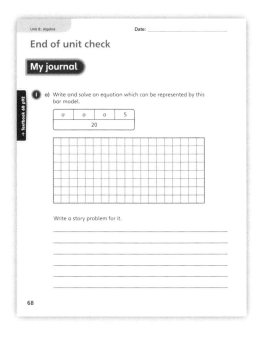

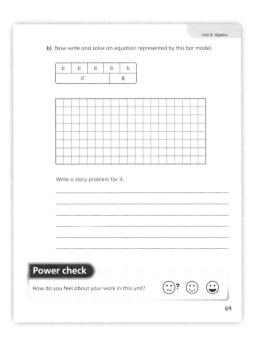

Date: _____

Use ratio language

1 Complete the sentences.

For every ☐ 1 apple there are ☐ 2 pears. *A : P* *1:2* ✓

For every ☐ 2 pears there is ☐ 1 apple. *2:1* ✓

2 Draw 3 apples for every 1 banana.

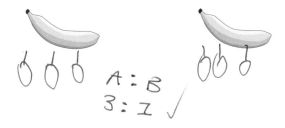

A : B
3 : 1 ✓

3 Complete the sentences for the pencils and rulers.

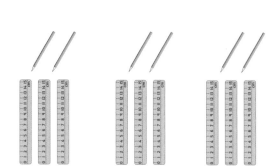

a) For every ☐ 3 rulers there are ☐ 2 pencils. *R : P* *3:2* *R:P* ¹/₂ ✓

b) For every ☐ 2 pencils there are ☐ 3 rulers. *2:3* *P:R*

6

4 Draw diagrams to represent the following ratio sentences.

a) There are 3 triangles for every 1 circle.

b) There are 2 squares for every 5 circles.

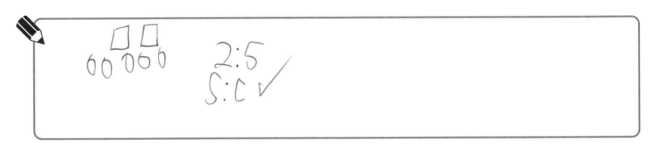

5 a) Draw a line to match the correct shape to its corresponding ratio statement.

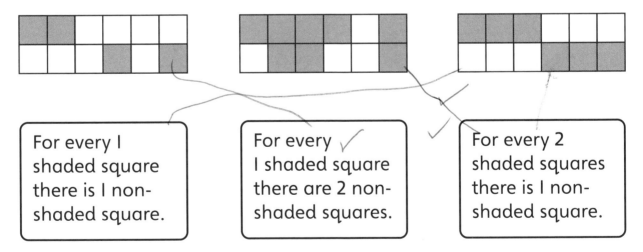

For every 1 shaded square there is 1 non-shaded square.

For every 1 shaded square there are 2 non-shaded squares.

For every 2 shaded squares there is 1 non-shaded square.

b) Shade squares in the rectangle to match the description below.

'For every 1 non-shaded square there are 5 shaded squares.'

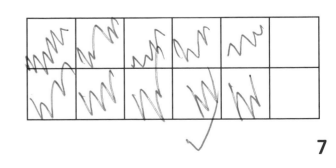

6 **a)** A tower is made up of red and white cubes.

Rohi says, 'For every 3 red cubes there is
1 white cube.'

I will make sized
towers of cubes to
help me.

CHALLENGE

Make or draw 2 possible towers of cubes.

R R R
W
3:1 R:W

R : W
3 : 1

R R R R R R
W W
6:2 R:W

R = W
6 = 2

b) The fraction that is red in each tower is $\frac{3}{4}$.

Discuss with a partner whether you agree or disagree with
the statement.

Reflect

What can you see? Write your answer as a ratio sentence.

Date: _____

Introduce the ratio symbol

1 At the farm there are 12 chicks and 3 hens.

What is the ratio of chicks to hens?

For every ☐ 4 chicks there is ☐ 1 hen.

C   H
4 : 1 ✓

Or, the ratio of chicks to hens is ☐ 4 : ☐ 1 . ✓

Pig

C : H : P
4 : 1 : 4.

2 a) What is the ratio of jars to tins?

Tins

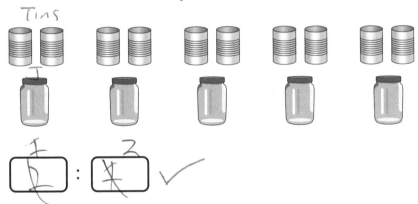

☐ 1 : ☐ 3 ✓

b) What is the ratio of jars to tins?

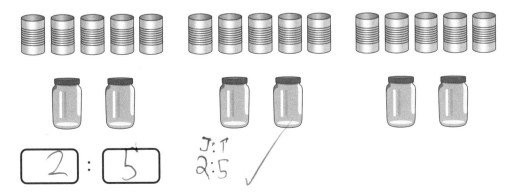

☐ 2 : ☐ 5

J : T
2 : 5 ✓

3 What is the ratio of shaded to non-shaded squares in each diagram?

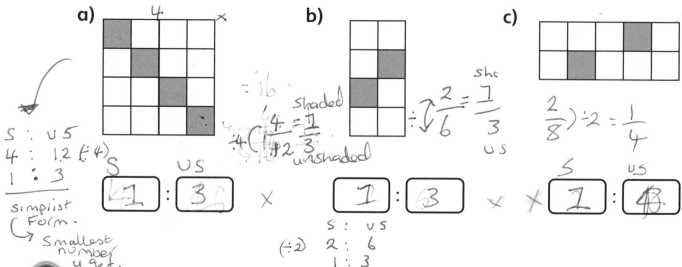

a)

S : U5
4 : 12 (÷4)
1 : 3

simplist
(Form.
↳ smallest
number
u get.

$\boxed{4 \; 1}$: $\boxed{3}$

b)

$= 16$
Shaded
$\frac{4}{4} = \frac{1}{...}$

$\frac{2}{6} = \frac{1}{3}$ she

U S

$\boxed{I}$: $\boxed{3}$

S : U S
(÷2) 2 : 6
1 : 3

c)

$\frac{2}{8}) \div 2 = \frac{1}{4}$

S   U S

$\boxed{I}$: $\boxed{4}$

4 In each box, draw triangles and circles to show the ratio.

Draw more than six shapes in each box.

<table>
<tr><td>

a) The ratio of triangles to circles
is 3 : 1.

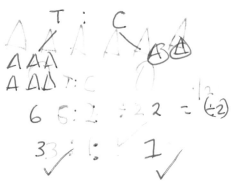

T : C

6 6 : 2 ÷ 2 = (÷2)

3 : 1

</td><td>

c) The ratio of triangles to circles
is 1 : 3.

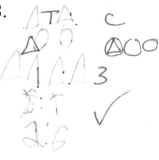

T : C

3

</td></tr>
<tr><td>

b) The ratio of triangles to circles
is 3 : 2.

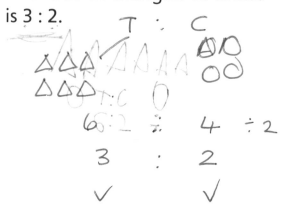

T : C

6 : 2 ÷   4 ÷ 2

3 : 2

</td><td>

d) The ratio of triangles to circles
is 1 : 4.

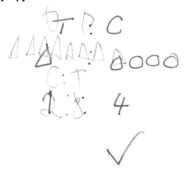

T : C

2 : 8 4

</td></tr>
</table>

5 The ratio of the length of a pencil to the length of a straw is 1 : 2.

① ②

a) Is the pencil longer than the straw? Explain your answer.

P : S
1 : 2

No the straw is two times longer.

b) Is the straw twice as long as the pencil? Explain your answer.

P : S
×6 (1 : 2 × ×6 length=6
   6 : 12

6 Ambika mixes $1\frac{1}{2}$ litres of orange juice and lemonade.

She uses 250 ml of orange juice.

What is the ratio of orange juice to lemonade?

The ratio of orange juice to lemonade is ☐ : ☐ .

CHALLENGE

Reflect

'The ratio 2 : 1 is the same as the ratio 1 : 2.' Do you agree? Explain your answer.

Date: _____

Use ratio

1 Lee draws some shapes.

For every 3 squares he draws 4 circles.

Here is part of the diagram Lee has drawn.

a) Complete Lee's diagram.

b) How many circles does Lee draw in total?

2 A jar contains strawberry sweets and lime sweets.

For every 2 strawberry sweets, there are 3 lime sweets.

There are 18 lime sweets in the jar.

Use the table to help you work out how many strawberry sweets are in the jar.

Strawberry	Lime
2	3
4	6

3 A box contains some buttons.

For every 2 plain buttons there are 5 stripey buttons.

If there are 12 plain buttons in the box, how many stripey buttons are there?

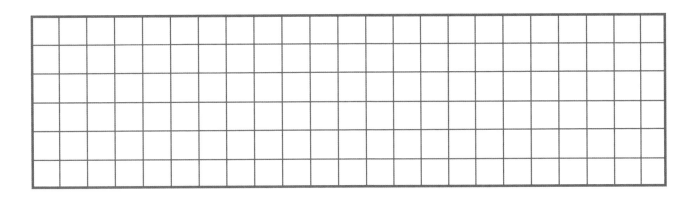

4 In a fish tank, for every 1 clown fish there are 4 box fish.

If the tank contains 7 clown fish, how many box fish are there?

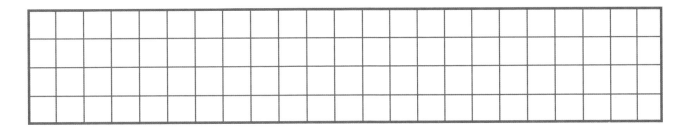

5 A pattern is made up of squares and rectangles.

For every 2 squares there are 5 rectangles.

Explain to a partner why the pattern cannot have 7 squares.

_____

_____

_____

_____

13

6 For every 9 cows there are 5 sheep.

There are 36 cows. How many more cows than sheep are there?

7 Josh has some 5p and 10p coins.

For every three 5p coins, Josh has one 10p coin.

Josh has 80p in 10p coins. How much money does Josh have in total?

CHALLENGE

Reflect

In a bag of balloons, there are 3 large balloons for every 4 small balloons.

Are there more large or more small balloons in the bag? How do you know?

Scale drawing

1 The diagram shows a plan of an office space drawn on 1 cm squared paper.

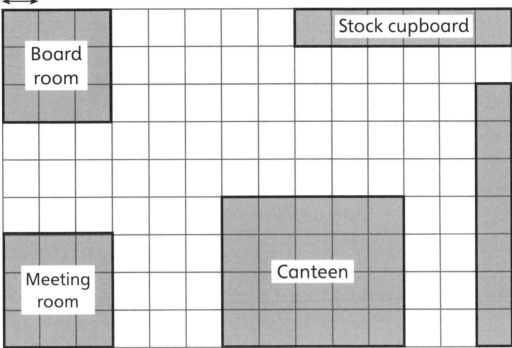

On the plan, 1 cm represents 2 m in real life.

a) Complete the scale.

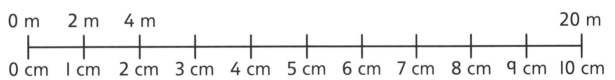

b) What is the length of the canteen in real life? ☐ m

c) The board room is a square.

What is the actual perimeter of the board room? ☐ m

d) A rectangular rug is added to the office. It is 2 m × 5 m.

Draw and label the rug on the plan.

2 Kate draws a plan of her classroom to scale. She uses the scale 2 cm : I m.

a) What does the scale mean?

Every ☐ cm on the plan represents ☐ m in real life.

b) Complete the scale.

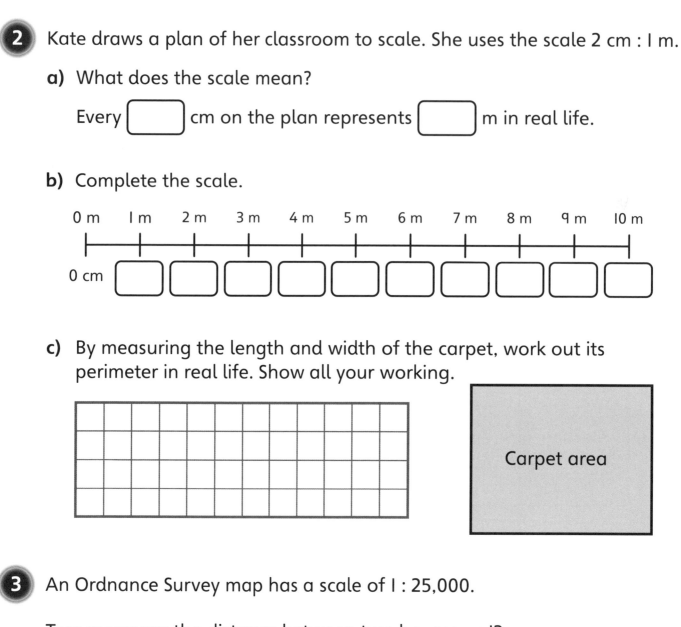

c) By measuring the length and width of the carpet, work out its perimeter in real life. Show all your working.

3 An Ordnance Survey map has a scale of I : 25,000.

Tom measures the distance between two houses as I2 cm.

What is the actual distance between the two houses?

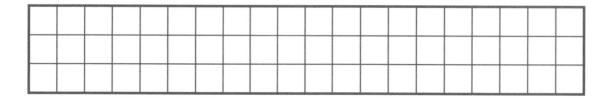

4 Lexi and Jen are cycling from Wakefield to York.

They work out a route on the map that is 11 cm long. The scale on the map is 1 cm : 5 km.

What is the actual length of their route?

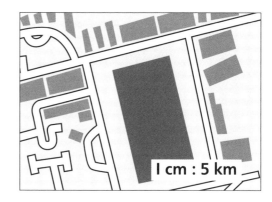

1 cm : 5 km

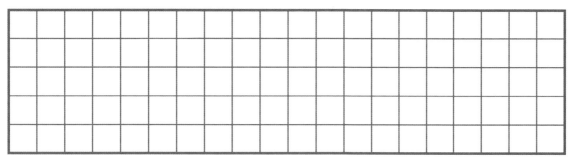

5 The perimeters of these two shaded shapes are equal in length.

CHALLENGE

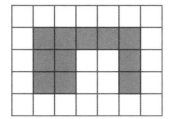

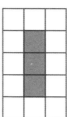

Scale 1 : 20

Scale 1 : ⬜

What is the missing scale? Explain your method to a partner.

Reflect

What is the same about these scales? What is different? Discuss with a partner.

1 : 200   1 cm : 2 m

Date: _____

Scale factors

 1 Zac draws a line 9 cm long.

9 cm

a) Mo draws a line 18 cm long.

How many times longer is Mo's line than Zac's?

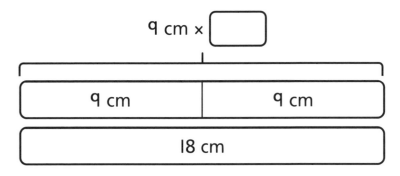

9 cm × ☐

| 9 cm | 9 cm |

| 18 cm |

Mo's line is ☐ times longer than Zac's.

So, the scale factor of enlargement is ☐ .

b) Olivia draws a line 45 cm long.

How many times longer is Olivia's line than Zac's?

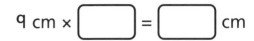

9 cm × ☐ = ☐ cm

| 9 cm | 9 cm |

| 45 cm |

Olivia's line is ☐ times as long as Zac's.

So, the scale factor of enlargement is ☐ .

2 Draw each of these shapes after they have been enlarged by a scale factor of 2.

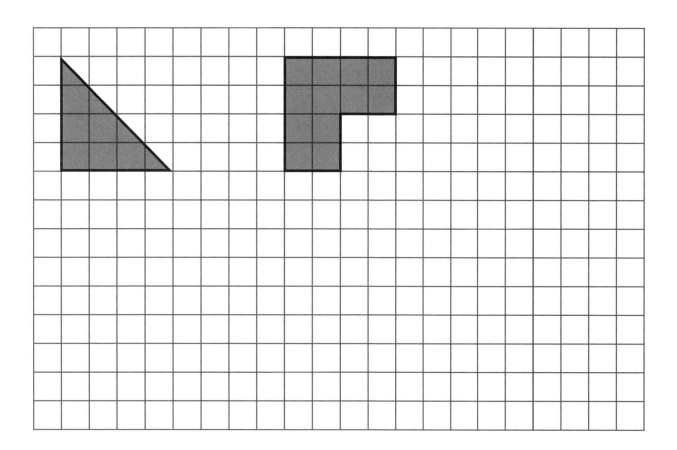

3 Some rectangles have been enlarged by different scale factors. The table shows what happens to the length of the rectangles. Complete the table.

Rectangle	Original length	Scale factor of enlargement	New length
A	6 cm	4	
B		5	60 cm
C	18 cm	$\frac{1}{2}$	
D	18 cm	$1\frac{1}{2}$	
E	5 cm		5 m

4 Reena says she has enlarged this shape by a scale factor of 3. Is Reena correct? Explain your answer to a partner.

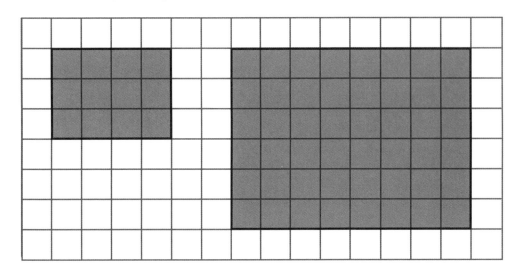

_____

_____

5 Find the scale factor of enlargement.

CHALLENGE

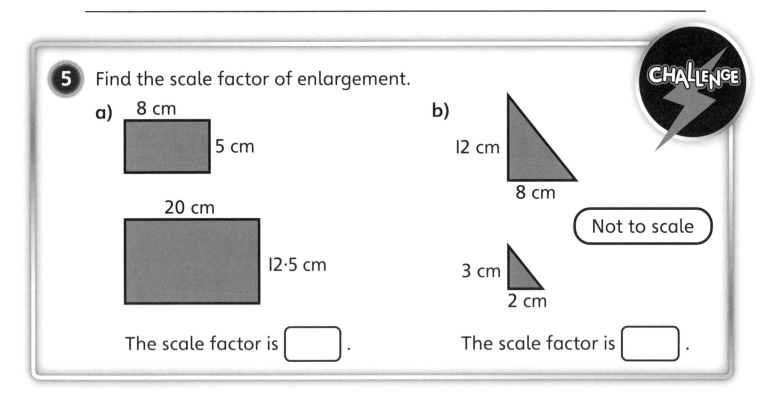

a) 8 cm
5 cm

20 cm
12·5 cm

b) 12 cm
8 cm

Not to scale

3 cm
2 cm

The scale factor is ☐ .

The scale factor is ☐ .

Reflect

Draw a shape on a whiteboard or in your workbook and ask your partner to enlarge the shape by a scale factor of 3. Take it in turns.

Date: _____

Similar shapes

1 Are these shapes similar?

If so, what is the scale factor? Explain your answer.

a)

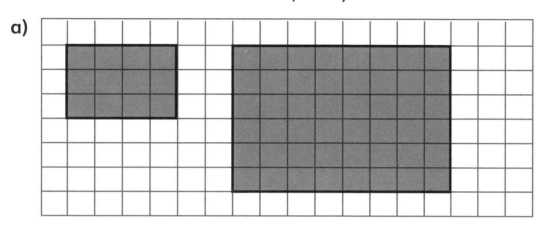

_____

_____

b)

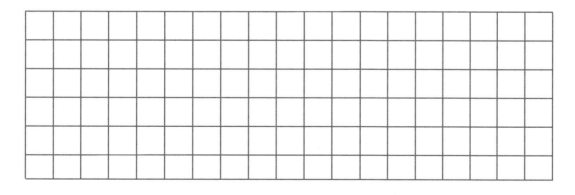

_____

_____

2 Draw two triangles that are similar.

3 These pairs of shapes are similar.

For each pair of shapes, find the scale factor of enlargement and then find the missing side.

a)

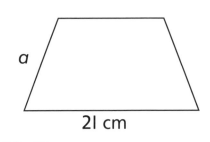

The scale factor is ☐ .

The length of side *a* is

☐ cm.

(Not to scale)

b)

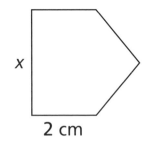

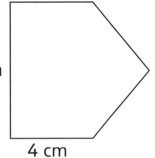

The scale factor is ☐ .

The length of side *b* is

☐ cm.

4 These shapes are all similar. Find the missing sides.

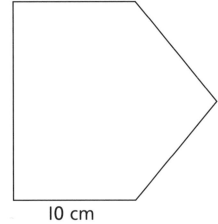

x = ☐ cm   *y* = ☐ cm

5 These two parallelograms are similar.

CHALLENGE

a) What is the ratio of side *a* to side *b*?   ⬚ : ⬚

b) A third, similar parallelogram has side *c*. The ratio of *a* : *c* is 1 : 3.
   Draw the third parallelogram on the grid.

Reflect

Two sides in two similar shapes are in the ratio 1 : 4. What else do you know?

_____

_____

_____

Date: _____

Ratio problems

1 There are 30 slices of cake.

For every 1 slice of carrot cake there are 5 slices of lemon cake.

How many slices of each cake are there?

Complete the bar model to help you work out the answer.

Carrot [   ]

Lemon [| | | |] } 30

There are [   ] slices of carrot cake and [   ] slices of lemon cake.

2 Mr Lopez counts 63 balls in the PE cupboard.

For every 2 footballs there are 5 tennis balls.

How many of each ball are there?

There are [   ] footballs and [   ] tennis balls.

3 Shade in the rectangle to show 3 shaded squares for every 5 non-shaded squares.

4 There are 40 socks in a drawer.

The ratio of spotty to plain socks is 3 : 2.

a) How many spotty socks are there?

b) How many pairs of plain socks can be made?

Unit 7: Ratio and proportion, Lesson 7

5 Zac and Jamie share £72 that their Grandma has given them.

The ratio of Zac's share to Jamie's share is 7 : 5.

How much more money does Zac receive than Jamie? £ [   ]

6 Bella and Aki are each thinking of a different number.

The ratio of Bella's number to Aki's number is 3 : 7.

The difference between their numbers is 560.

What is the sum of their numbers?

CHALLENGE

Reflect

Explain the method you would use to share 60 into the ratio 2 : 3.

26

Problem solving – ratio and proportion

→ Textbook 6B p36

1 5 pencils cost 60p.

How much do 7 pencils cost?

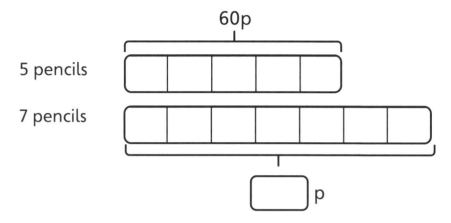

60p

5 pencils

7 pencils

☐ p

2 Eight identical, square paving slabs are laid to make a patio.

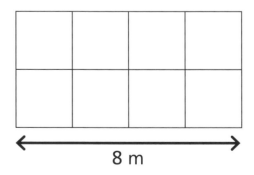

8 m

The length of the patio is 8 m.

What is the perimeter of the patio? ☐ m

3 Toshi is making pancakes. He uses a recipe for 4 pancakes.

Pancake recipe

Makes 4 pancakes

100 g flour

2 eggs

300 ml milk

1 tbsp oil

Pancake recipe

Makes 12 pancakes

☐ g flour

☐ eggs

☐ ml milk

☐ tbsp oil

a) Complete the recipe for 12 pancakes.

b) Toshi wants to make 10 pancakes. How much flour does he need?

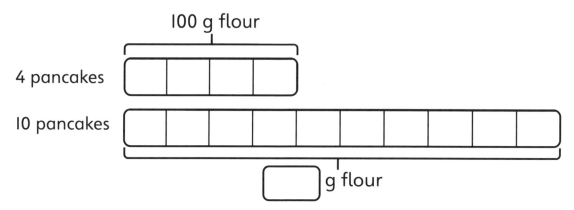

100 g flour

4 pancakes

10 pancakes

☐ g flour

c) How much milk does Toshi need to make 9 pancakes? ☐ ml

d) Toshi has 370 g of flour. What is the greatest number of pancakes he can make? ☐

4 3 bags of chips cost £3·60. 2 pieces of fish cost £5·60.

How much do 3 pieces of fish and 6 bags of chips cost?

£ [ ]

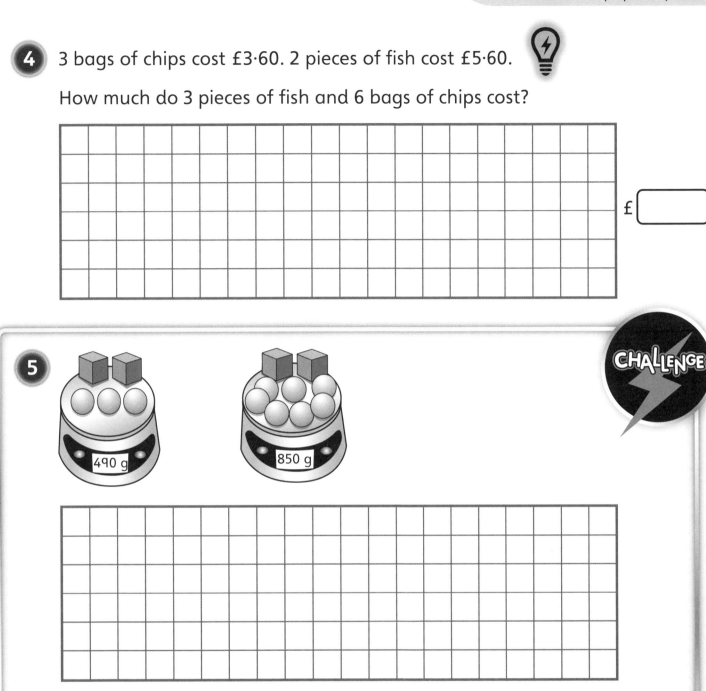

5

CHALLENGE

490 g

850 g

What is the mass of 5 cubes? [ ] g

Reflect

6 identical chocolates weigh 120 g.

Explain to a partner two ways you can work out the mass of 9 chocolates.

Date: _____

Problem solving – ratio and proportion ❷

Choose the method you want to use.

1 A florist is making a bouquet of flowers.

For every 4 roses in the bouquet there are 3 lilies.

There are 16 roses. How many lilies are there?

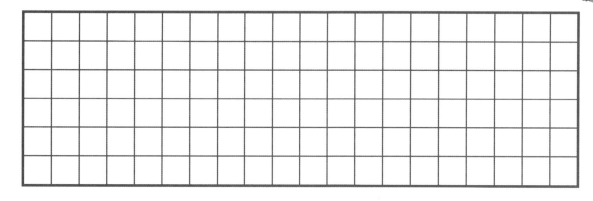

2 A bag contains a mix of mint and strawberry sweets.

The ratio of mint to strawberry sweets is 4 : 1.

a) How many times more mint sweets are there than strawberry sweets?

Explain how you know.

_____

_____

b) There are 32 mint sweets in the bag.

How many strawberry sweets are in the bag? ⬚

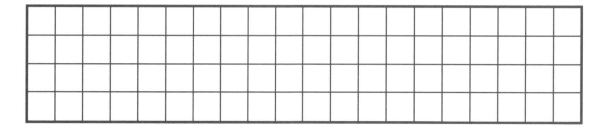

30

3 Reena and Richard share a chocolate bar.

For every 3 squares of chocolate Reena eats, Richard eats 2 squares.

Richard eats 16 squares of chocolate.

How many squares of chocolate are there in the whole bar? ☐

Reena ☐
Richard ☐
?
16

4 The total mass of some flour and sugar is 525 g.

There is four times as much flour as sugar.

How much does the sugar weigh? ☐ g

Flour ☐
Sugar ☐
525 g
?

5 In a box of toy bricks, there are 4 red bricks for every 2 blue and 1 yellow.

There are 5 yellow bricks. How many bricks are there altogether? ☐

6 In a bag of marbles, there are 4 blue marbles for every 1 green marble.

There are 15 more blue marbles than green marbles.

How many blue marbles are there?

7 Lexi catches three times as many fish as Luis.

Luis catches another 15 fish and now has 3 more fish than Lexi.

CHALLENGE

How many fish do they catch altogether?

Reflect

Explain why bar models are helpful for solving problems like these.

Date: _____

End of unit check

My journal

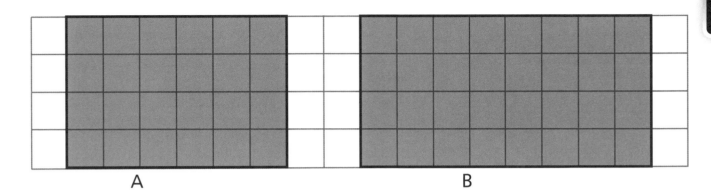

A   B

a) Andy says, 'When shape A is enlarged by a scale factor of 2, you get shape B.'

Is Andy correct? Explain your answer.

_____

_____

_____

b) What is the ratio of the sides in two shapes, if the first shape has been enlarged by a scale factor of 2 to make the second shape? Explain your answer.

_____

_____

Power check

How do you feel about your work in this unit?

Power play

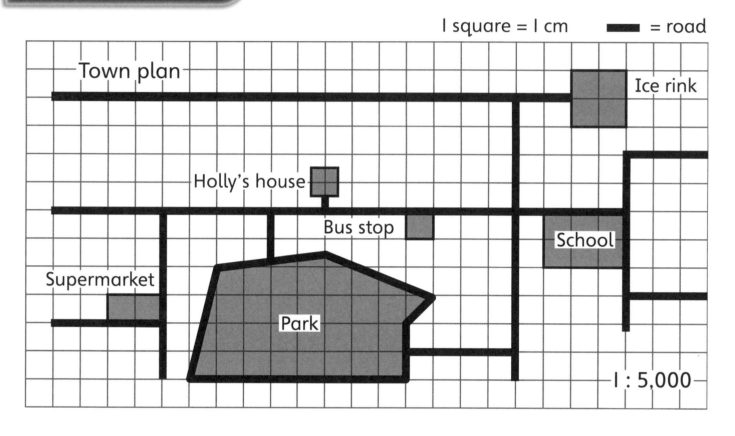

I square = I cm   ━━ = road

Town plan

Ice rink

Holly's house

Bus stop

School

Supermarket

Park

1 : 5,000

a) What does I cm on the plan represent in real life? How do you know?

_____

b) Find the shortest distance between the path outside Holly's house and the bus stop.

Explain your method.

_____

_____

c) Holly walks 350 m, the shortest distance from her house to the swimming pool.

Show two different locations on the plan where the swimming pool could be.

Date: _____

Unit 8: Algebra, Lesson 1

Find a rule – one step

1 Complete the table for each function machine.

a)

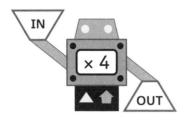

Input	1	2	3	5	8	p
Output						

b)

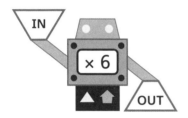

Input	1	2	5	11	18	q
Output	6					

2 Aki makes some fairy cakes.
Each cake has 3 stars on top.

a) Complete the table.

Number of cakes	1	2	3	5	10	100	1,500
Number of stars	1 × 3 = 3						

b) Write the rule for *n* fairy cakes.

For *n* fairy cakes, you need ☐ × ☐ stars.

35

Textbook 6B p48

3 Draw a line to match each repeating pattern with the rule for *n*.

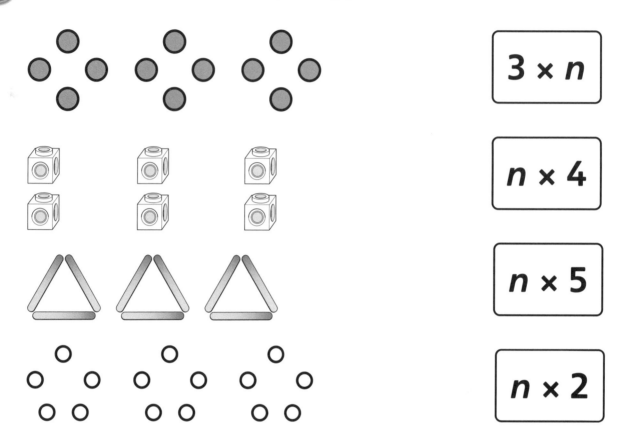

$$3 \times n$$

$$n \times 4$$

$$n \times 5$$

$$n \times 2$$

4 **a)** Zac started his painting 30 minutes before Kate. Complete the table for how long they have been painting.

Minutes Zac has been painting	45	50	90		*m*	
Minutes Kate has been painting				90		*y*

Complete these rules.

b) If Zac has been painting for *m* minutes, Kate has been painting for

_____

c) If Kate has been painting for *y* minutes, Zac has been painting for

_____

5 **a)** Complete the rules.

The number of legs on *b* spiders is _____ .

The number of wheels on *v* tricycles is _____ .

The number of days in *m* weeks is _____ .

The number of weeks in *k* years is _____ .

b) What could this rule be for?

The number of _____ is 365 × *d*.

6 Complete the tables. What are the rules?

CHALLENGE

1	3	12	15·5	*n*
5	7	16		

1	2	4	8	*y*
	5	10	20	

_____

_____

Reflect

What is the same and what is different about the rules *a* × 5 and 5 + *a*?

_____

_____

_____

Date: _____

Find a rule – two steps

1 Complete the table.

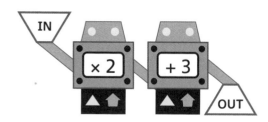

Input	1	2	3	4	5	n
Output	5					

2 **a)** Olivia has £25 in the bank. Each week she saves £3. Complete the table.

Week	1	2	3	4	5	10
Total savings	£28					

b) Complete the rule for how much Olivia has saved after y weeks.

After y weeks, Olivia has saved 25 + ⬚ × ⬚ pounds.

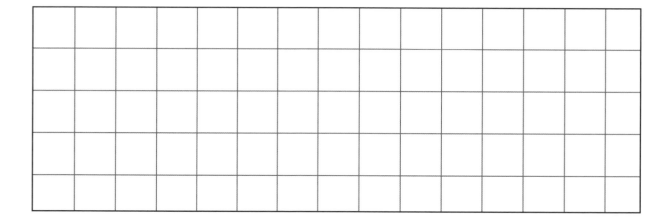

38

3 Here is a growing pattern of triangles made from sticks.

In a growing pattern, there is a rule for how it grows each time.

a) Complete the table.

Number of triangles	1	2	3	4	5	10	100
Number of sticks used							

b) Complete the rule.

To make n triangles, _____ sticks are used.

4 Ebo makes this pattern of houses. What is the rule for the number of sticks needed for a pattern with g houses?

For g houses, you need _____ sticks.

39

5 This pattern is made from squares and circles.

 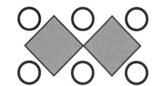 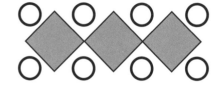

How many circles would be in the pattern that uses 100 squares?

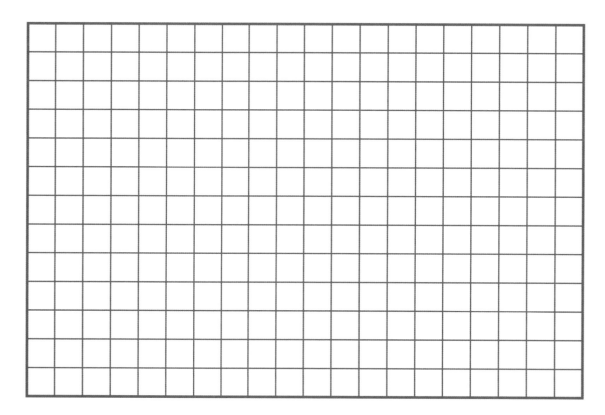

Reflect

Create a situation for the rule 100 − 3y.

Date: _____

Form expressions

↓ Textbook 6B p56

1 Richard has *p* pet guinea pigs. Luis has 2 more than Richard.

a) Complete the rule for how many guinea pigs Luis has.

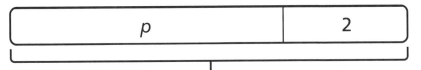

Number of Luis's guinea pigs

If Richard has *p* guinea pigs, Luis has ▢◯▢ guinea pigs.

b) Ambika has 3 times as many guinea pigs as Luis. Draw a bar model to represent how many guinea pigs Ambika has.

c) Calculate the number of guinea pigs Ambika has if Richard has 3 guinea pigs.

Ambika has ▢ guinea pigs.

d) Complete the table.

	Number of guinea pigs				
Richard	1	2	5	10	20
Luis	3				
Ambika	9				

2 Complete the table of inputs and outputs for each function machine.

a)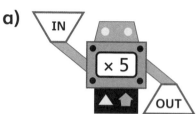

Input	1	2	3	5	10
Output					

If the input is a, the output is ⬚.

b)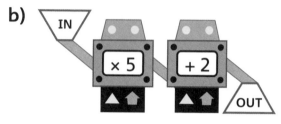

Input	1	2	3	5	10
Output					

If the input is b, the output is ⬚.

c)

Input	1	2	3	5	10
Output					

If the input is c, the output is ⬚.

d)

Input	1	2	3	5	10
Output					

If the input is d, the output is ⬚.

3 Max says: 'This is just the same as having a function machine with one function of − 10.'

Do you agree? Compare the outputs in the table.

Input	1	2	5	100	1,000	a
Output for − 10						
Output for + 5 − 15						

4 Kate is investigating two function machines. She inputs 10 and the output is 100. What could the functions be?

Explore different possibilities. Create a table of outputs.

a)

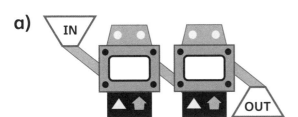

Input	10				n
Output	100				

b)

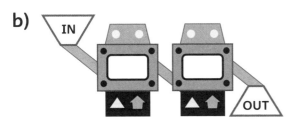

Input	10				n
Output	100				

Reflect

Emma has the rule 3m + 2. She wants to find the value when m is 100. Emma says: 'I will just find the output for 10, then multiply by 10.' Does this method work? Explore and explain.

Date: _____

Substitution

1 Reena has a pile of 5 pence coins.

a) Write the rule for the total value when the number of coins is *n*.

There are *n* 5 pence coins. The total value = ⬚ pence.

b) Complete the table for different values of *n*.

Number of 5p coins	Reena's total value
4	
5	
10	
30	
50	

2 To hire a squash court costs 20 pence per minute.

a) Write the rule for hiring the court for *n* minutes.

_____

b) Complete the table.

Time in minutes	Cost
n	
10	
30	
60	
120	

3 Complete the table.

	$t + 30$	$30 - t$	$30t$
$t = 5$			
$t = 10$			
$t = 30$			
$t = 0$			

4 Aki has to substitute $y = 7$ into $10y + 5$.

I can work this out by finding $7 + 5$ first, then multiplying by 10.

Aki

Does this work?

Explain your answer.

_____

_____

5 Explain how to choose values of y for the following rule, so that the result is a multiple of 10.

$100 - 5y$

_____

_____

_____

_____

45

6 Substitute different values for y into the expression $10y - y$.

When $y = 1$, $10y - y =$ ☐ .

When $y =$ ☐ , $10y - y =$ ☐ .

When _____ .

When _____ .

When _____ .

What do you notice? Explore and explain.

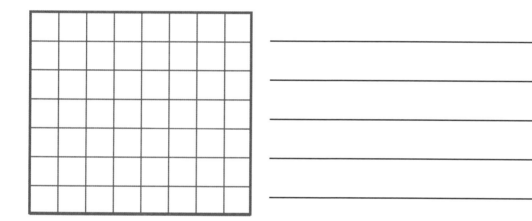

Reflect

Substitute different values for y in the rule $4 + 2y$. Explain why all the results are even.

Substitution ❷

1 **a)** Toshi cuts 5 equal lengths from 100 cm of ribbon. Each length is y cm.

Write the rule for the length of ribbon he has left.

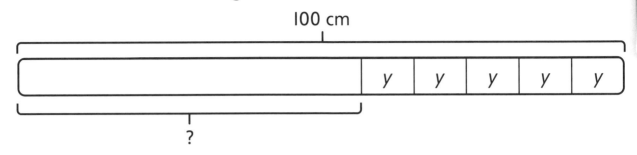

_____

b) How much ribbon is left if $y = 12$ cm? [ ] cm

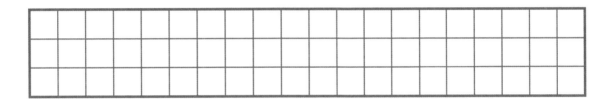

2 **a)** Write an expression for the total height of a tower with n blocks.

The total height is [ ] + [ ] n.

b) Calculate the total height when $n = 8$. [ ]

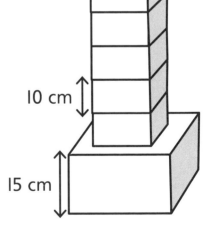

10 cm

15 cm

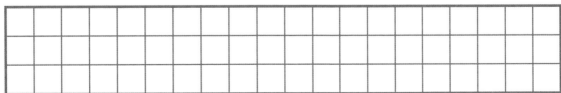

3 If $y = 100$

Complete the missing values on the bar models.

a)

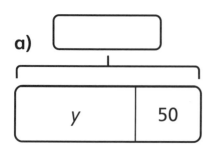

c)

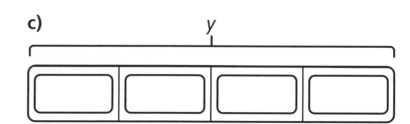

b)

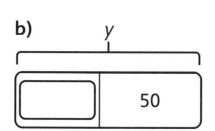

d)

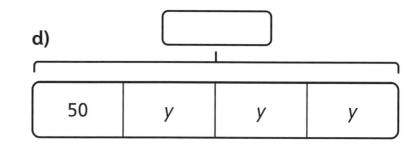

4 Match each expression with the equivalent meaning.

5 less than y

y more than 20

double y

$5 - y$

$y + 2$

$20 + y$

$2y$

$y \times y$

$y - 5$

5 Complete the table.

CHALLENGE

	Write an expression for each '?'	Substitute $n = 110$ into each expression. Calculate the value of '?'
n $\quad n \quad$ n 20 $\longleftarrow$? $\longrightarrow$		
n ▢ ▢ 10 ?		
n ▢ ▢ ▢ ▢ 10 ?		

Reflect

What is the value of $25 - 2y$ when y equals 3?
Draw a bar model to explain.

Date: _____

Formulae

1 Write an expression for the perimeter of each shape. Then calculate the perimeter by substituting $a = 4$ cm and $b = 5$ cm.

a)

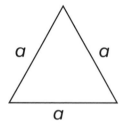

Formula: $3a$

Perimeter = ☐ cm

c)

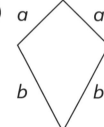

Formula: ☐

Perimeter = ☐ cm

b)

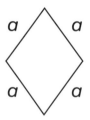

Formula: ☐

Perimeter = ☐ cm

d)

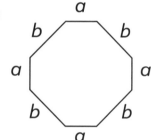

Formula: ☐

Perimeter = ☐ cm

2 A formula to calculate the number of inches in z feet is $12z$.

How many inches tall is each tower?

Tower A: 100 feet = ☐ inches

Tower B: 200 feet = ☐ inches

Tower C: 150 feet = ☐ inches

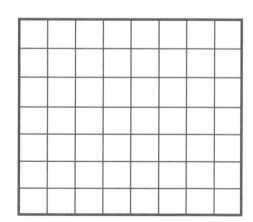

3 A scientist uses the formula $\boxed{\text{distance} = s \times t}$ to calculate the distance a rocket has travelled.

> Speed is measured in kilometres per hour (kph).

s stands for the speed in kph.

t stands for the time in hours.

Calculate the distance travelled when the rocket has been moving at a speed of 200 kph for 2 days.

The rocket has travelled ☐ km.

4 Max joins two of these squares together to make a new shape.

a
a   *a*
a

> The perimeter of the square is 4*a*, so the perimeter of my new shape is 8*a*.

Max

Do you agree with Max? Explain and show an example, substituting a value for *a*.

_____

_____

_____

5 Complete the calculation patterns using algebra.

CHALLENGE

a) $99 + 2 = 100 + 1$

$99 + 3 = 100 + 2$

$99 + 4 = 100 + \boxed{}$

$99 + 5 = 100 + \boxed{}$

$99 + a = 100 + \boxed{}$

b) $99 \times 1 = 100 \times 1 - 1$

$99 \times 2 = 100 \times 2 - 2$

$99 \times 3 = 100 \times 3 - \boxed{}$

$99 \times 4 = 100 \times \boxed{} - \boxed{}$

$99 \times b = 100 \times \boxed{} - \boxed{}$

Explain each pattern using words. Are both patterns always true?

_____

_____

_____

_____

_____

Reflect

Write a formula to show how to calculate the perimeter when $x = 10$ cm and $y = 8$ cm.

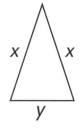

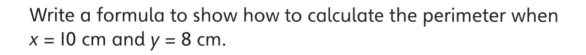

Form and solve equations

1 **a)** Substitute different values for a to find a solution to the equation.

$a + 150 = \boxed{237}$

If a is:	Then $a + 150$ is:
100	
200	

b) Substitute different values for b to solve the equation.

$150 - b = \boxed{103}$

If b is:	Then $150 - b$ is:
10	
20	
50	

c) Use the bar model to help you solve the equation $28 + c = 100$.

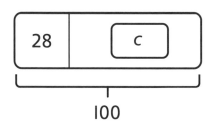

100

$c = \boxed{}$

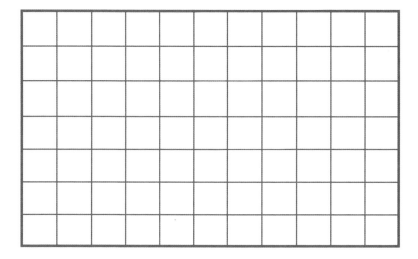

2 Solve the equations.

a) $a + 3 = 15$

$a =$ ⬚

c) $3a = 15$

$a =$ ⬚

b) $a - 3 = 15$

$a =$ ⬚

d) $a \div 3 = 15$

$a =$ ⬚

3 Solve each equation.

a) $v - 10 = 300$

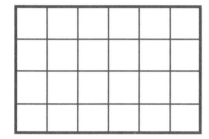

b) $300 = 10y$

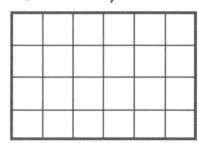

c) $z \div 10 = 300$

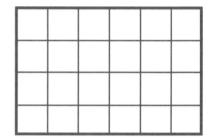

4 To solve $36 - f = 16$, Luis said: 'I worked out $16 + 36$, because I used the inverse.'

Is he correct? Show your reasoning using a diagram.

5 Write and solve an equation for each function machine.

CHALLENGE

a)

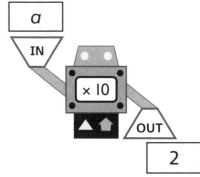

Equation: 10a = [ ]

Solution: a = [ ]

c)

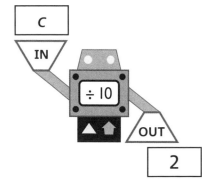

Equation: _____

Solution: _____

b)

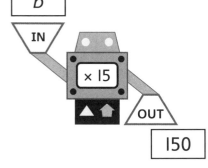

Equation: _____

Solution: _____

d)

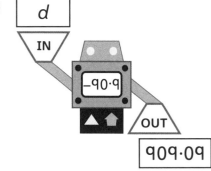

Equation: _____

Solution: _____

Reflect

Show two methods to solve $200 = y + 75$.

Date: _____

Solve one-step equations

1 Complete and solve the equations.

a)

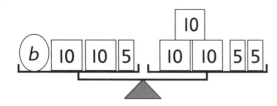

$b + 25 = 40$

Subtract [ ] from each scale.

$b =$ [ ]

b)

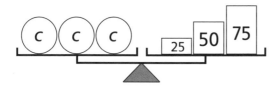

$3c =$ [ ]

Divide each side by [ ]

$c =$ [ ]

c)

a	45
100	

$a + 45 = 100$

$100 - 45 =$ [ ]

$a =$ [ ]

d)

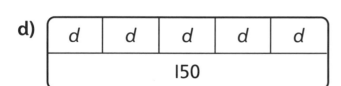

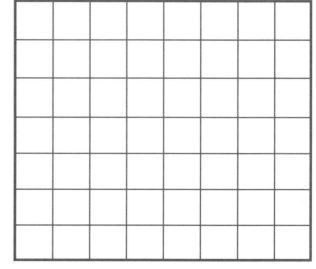

2 Match each model with the correct equation, then solve them.

a)

c	
50	25

$25 = 5c$

$c =$ ☐

b)

c	c	c	c	c
25				

$25 + c = 50$

$c =$ ☐

c)

25 25   c 25

$c - 25 = 50$

$c =$ ☐

3 Solve each equation.

a) $40 - f = 37$ $f =$ ☐

b) $g + 37·5 = 40$ $g =$ ☐

c) $400 = h + 37$ $h =$ ☐

d) $4,000 - i = 3,750$ $i =$ ☐

e) $4·4 = 40·4 - j$ $j =$ ☐

f) $4k = 4$ $k =$ ☐

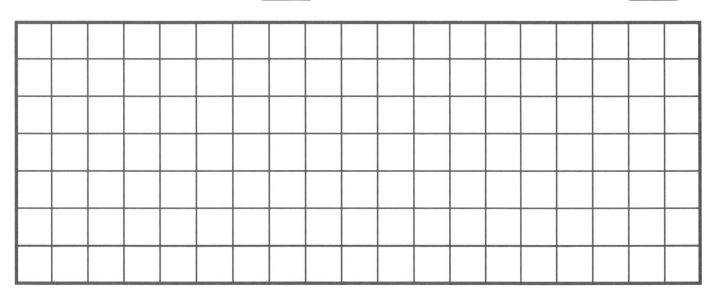

57

4 Choose five cards each time to make different equations.
Solve each equation. Show your workings.

CHALLENGE

| 240 | 24 | 80 | 8 | 100 | 10 | y | + | – | × | ÷ | = |

◻○◻○◻   ◻○◻○◻

◻○◻○◻   ◻○◻○◻

Reflect

Draw a diagram to represent the equation $100 - y = 90$.

Solve two-step equations

1 Solve $5c + 15 = 50$.

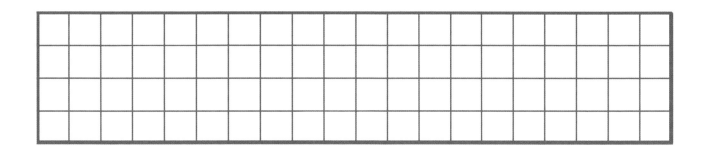

2 Solve the equation for each mystery number problem.

a)

I am thinking of a number. I multiply it by 3 and then add 2. Now I have 17.

Isla

$3a + 2 = 17$

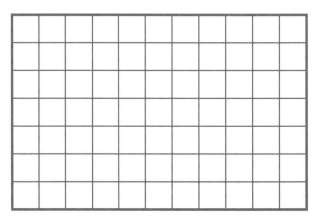

b)

I am thinking of a number. I multiply it by 4 and then add 80. Now I have 100.

Ebo

$4b + 80 = 100$

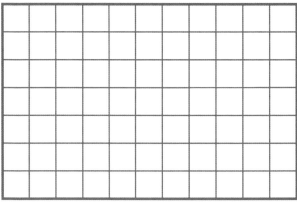

→ Textbook 6B p80

3 Look at the balance scales. Is Olivia correct?

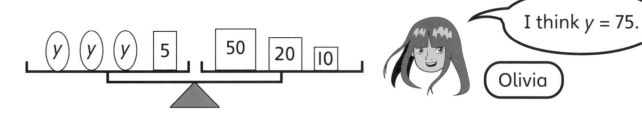

I think $y = 75$.

Olivia

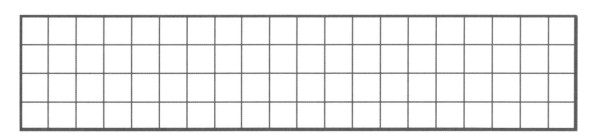

4 Bella has 50 stickers. Max has 6 packets of stickers and 3 more stickers. He has 1 more sticker than Bella.

Use n to represent the number of stickers in a packet.

Write an equation and solve to find n.

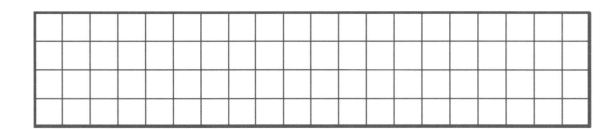

5 Solve each equation.

a) $4a - 30 = 50$

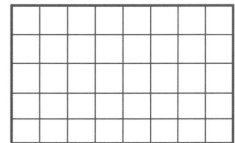

b) $2c - 50 = 80$

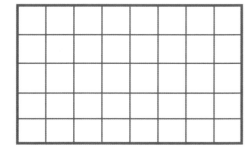

6 Write an equation for each function machine, then solve each one.

CHALLENGE

a) y

IN

$\div 5$ $- 5$

OUT

6

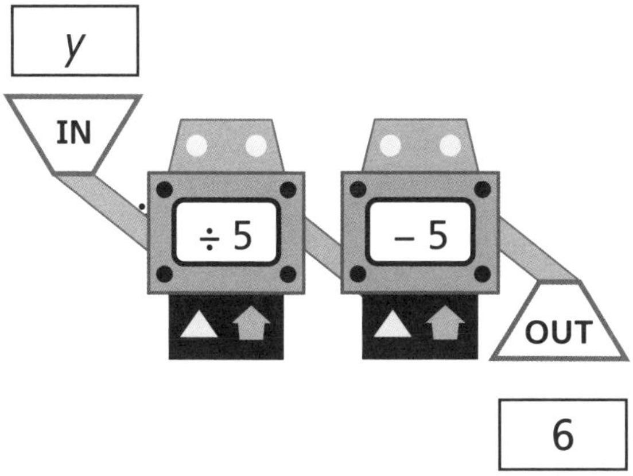

b) z

IN

$+ 20$ $\times 10$

OUT

1,000

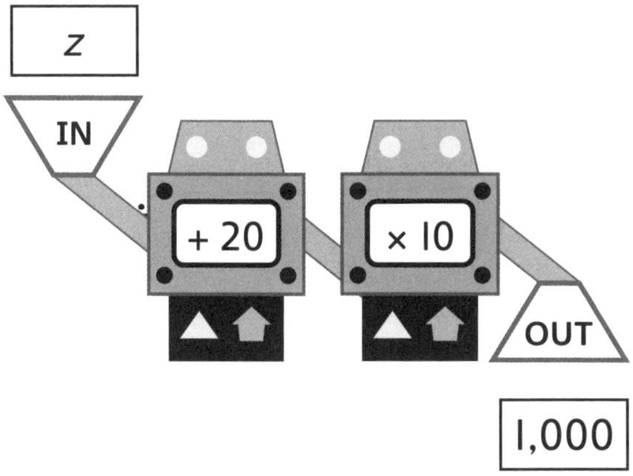

Reflect

Draw a bar model to represent the equation $5y + 5 = 25$.

Date: _____

Find pairs of values

1 **a)** Look at the balance scales. Explain why $a + b = 4$.

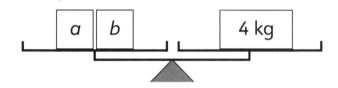

_____

_____

b) Find five different solutions for a and b.

a = ?	b = ?

2 A rectangle has a perimeter of 12 cm.

Each side is a whole number of centimetres.

Find all of the solutions.

Perimeter	j = ?	k = ?
12 cm		
12 cm		
12 cm		

3 A rectangular playground has an area of 100 m².

Each side is a whole number of metres.

e

f

(Not to scale)

a) Explain why *e* × *f* = 100.

_____

_____

b) Find 5 different solutions for *e* and *f*.

e = ?	*f* = ?

4 Plot the solutions for each equation on the grid.

Draw a straight line for each equation.

a) $x + y = 9$

b) $y - x = 2$

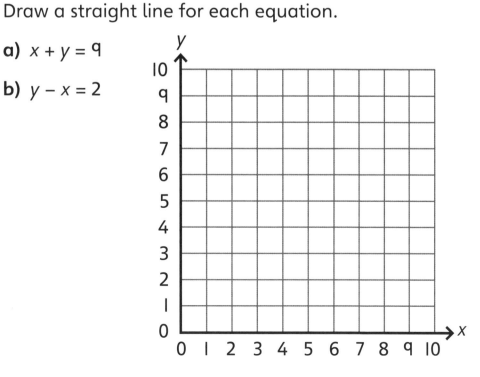

5 **a)** Four odd numbers add up to 20.

odd + odd + odd + odd = 20

Each number is different.

Find all the possible solutions.

b) odd + even − odd = 2

All the numbers are less than 10. All the numbers are different.

Find all the possible solutions.

Reflect

Describe a strategy for finding all possible solutions to an equation.

Date: _____

Solve problems with two unknowns

1 Alex has some 2p coins and some 5p coins. In total she has 25p. How many of each coin could she have?

Find all possible solutions.

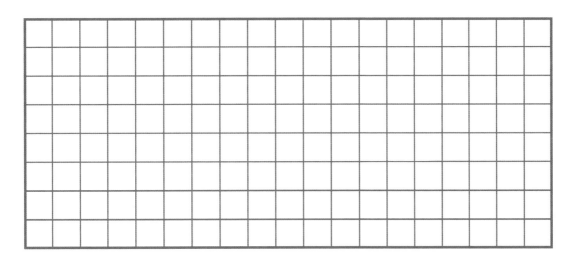

2 A rectangle has a perimeter of 24 cm and an area less than 30 cm². Both the length and the width are whole numbers. Find all possible solutions.

a

b (Not to scale)

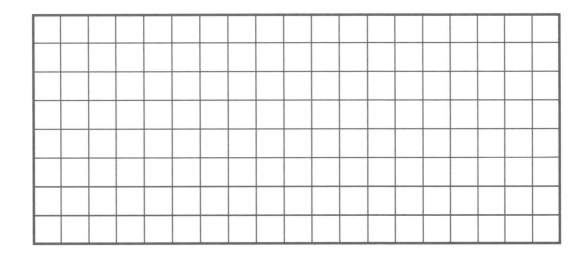

65

3 There are some fish in a tank. Blue fish have 4 spots. Red fish have 8 spots. In total there are 32 spots.

Use *b* for the number of blue fish and *r* for the number of red fish. Write an equation and find all possible solutions.

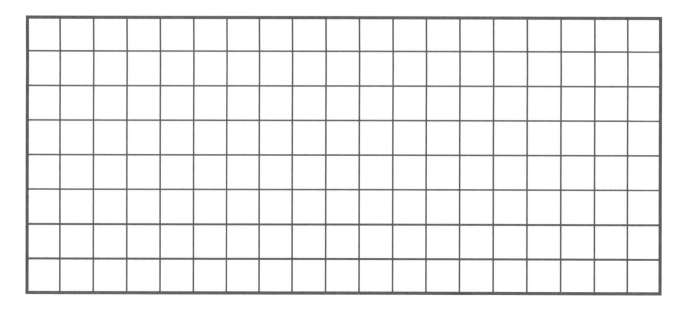

4 Find five different **whole number** solutions to each of the equations. Describe any patterns you notice.

a) $2a - b = 10$

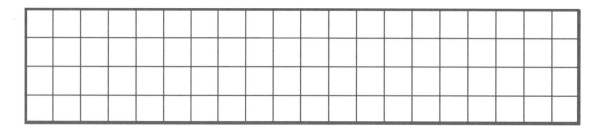

b) $50 + c = d - 150$

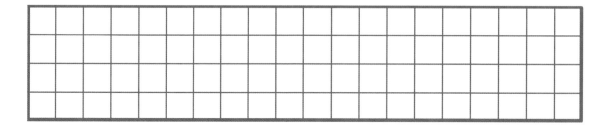

66

5 Bella and Danny each choose two numbers less than 20.

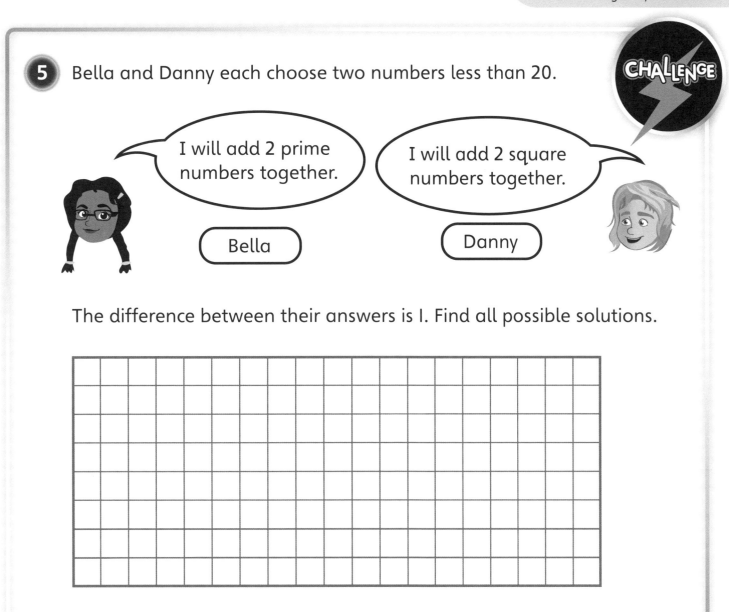

I will add 2 prime numbers together.

Bella

I will add 2 square numbers together.

Danny

CHALLENGE

The difference between their answers is 1. Find all possible solutions.

Reflect

Write an equation that has more than three solutions.

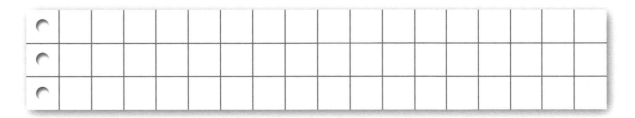

Date: _____

End of unit check

My journal

↑ Textbook 6B p92

1 **a)** Write and solve an equation which can be represented by this bar model.

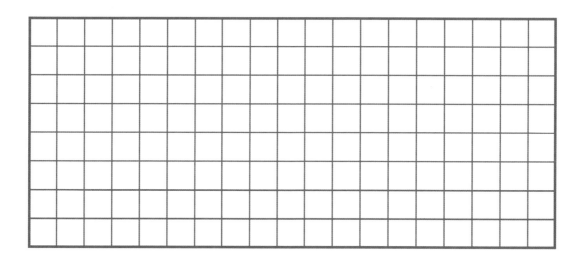

a	a	a	5
20			

Write a story problem for it.

_____

_____

_____

_____

_____

b) Now write and solve an equation represented by this bar model.

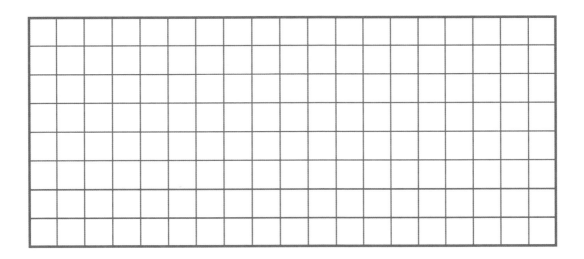

Write a story problem for it.

_____

_____

_____

_____

_____

_____

Power check

How do you feel about your work in this unit?

Power puzzle

How many rectangles can you see in this grid?

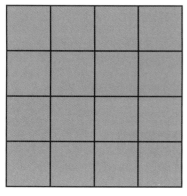

I can find some that are this size.

Don't forget that squares are a type of rectangle.

Can you find all the possible rectangles hidden in the grid?

Show your strategy for finding them all.

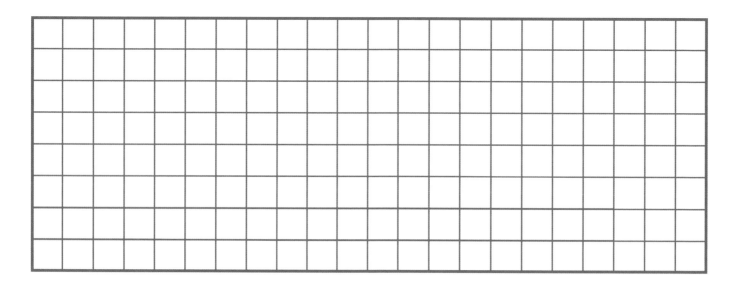

Investigate this for different-sized grids. Can you predict how many you can find, based on the size of the grid?

Place value to 3 decimal places

1 What numbers are shown?

a)

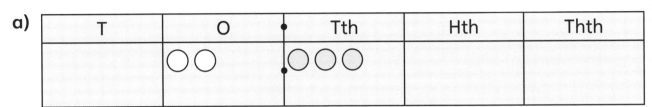

T	O	Tth	Hth	Thth

[ ]

b)

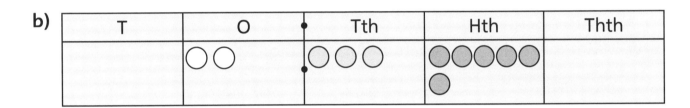

T	O	Tth	Hth	Thth

[ ]

c)

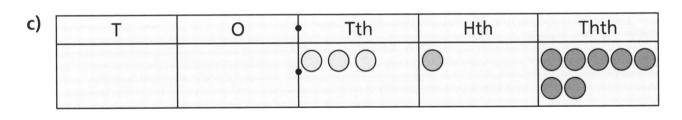

T	O	Tth	Hth	Thth

[ ]

d)

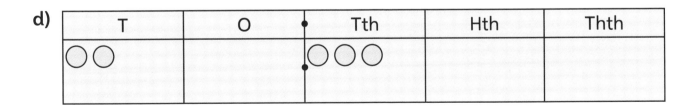

T	O	Tth	Hth	Thth

[ ]

2 **a)** Draw counters to make the number 1·46.

T	O	Tth	Hth	Thth

b) Draw counters to make the number 2·503.

T	O	Tth	Hth	Thth

3 What is the value of each underlined digit?

a) 7·3<u>6</u> _____

d) 3<u>5</u>·7 _____

b) 1·<u>5</u>04 _____

e) <u>4</u>09·26 _____

c) 0·39<u>2</u> _____

f) 0·0<u>4</u>5 _____

4 Complete the part-whole models.

a)

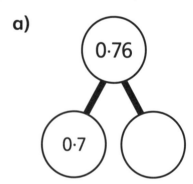

c)

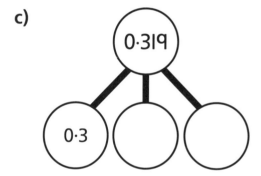

b)

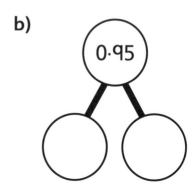

d)

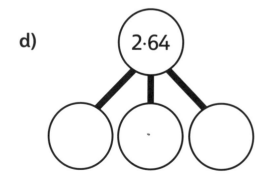

5 Complete the partitions.

a) 2·45 = 2 + 0·4 + ☐

b) 7·125 = 7 + ☐ + ☐ + ☐

c) 0·518 = 0·5 + ☐ + ☐

d) 86·09 = 80 + ☐ + ☐

e) 0·067 = ☐ + ☐

f) ☐ = 0·5 + 0·08 + 0·009

g) ☐ = 6 + 0·03 + 0·007

6

O	•	Tth	Hth	Thth
3	•	1	9	6

CHALLENGE

a) What is one-tenth more than the number? ☐

b) What is one-hundredth more than the number? ☐

c) What is one-thousandth more than the number? ☐

Reflect

Discuss with a partner two things you have learnt about decimals today.

Date: _____

Round decimals

1 Round each number to the nearest whole number.
Use the number lines to help you.

a)

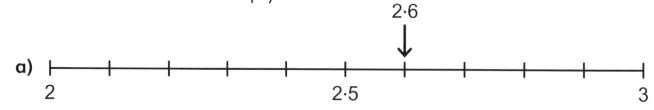

2·6 rounded to the nearest whole number is ⬚.

b)

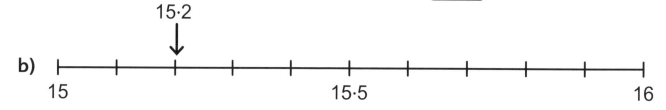

15·2 rounded to the nearest whole number is ⬚.

c)

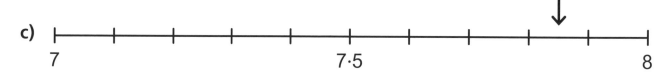

7·85 rounded to the nearest whole number is ⬚.

d)

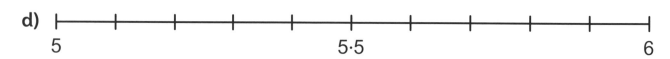

5·43 rounded to the nearest whole number is ⬚.

5·5 rounded to the nearest whole number is ⬚.

5·741 rounded to the nearest whole number is ⬚.

2 Round each number to the nearest tenth.

a)
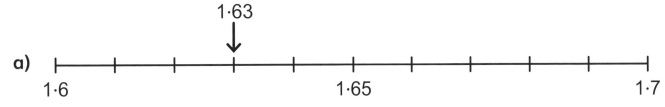

1·63 rounded to the nearest tenth is ☐ .

b)
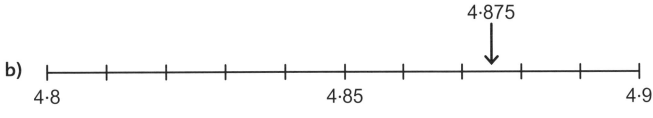

4·875 rounded to the nearest tenth is ☐ .

3 Complete the table.

Number	Rounded to the nearest whole number	Rounded to 1 decimal place
3·72		
4·18		
39·16		
0·871		
3·025		

4 Round each number to 2 decimal places.

a) 1·712 ☐

b) 1·715 ☐

5 Emma rounds 12·47 to the nearest whole number.

I first round the 4 up to a 5 as the 7 is greater than 5. I now have 12·5.

12·5 rounds up to 13.

Emma

What mistake has Emma made? Discuss with a partner.

_____

_____

_____

6 **a)** Write down three numbers that round to 6·55 to 2 decimal places. ☐ , ☐ , ☐

b) What is the smallest number that rounds to 6·55 to 2 decimal places? ☐

c) What is the greatest number that rounds to 6·55 to 2 decimal places? ☐

CHALLENGE

Reflect

Is Richard correct? Discuss with a partner.

To round a decimal to the nearest whole number, you look at the first number after the decimal point.

Richard

Date: _____

Add and subtract decimals

1 Complete the number sentences.

a) 1·8 + 5·4 = ☐

	T	O •	Tth	Hth
		1 •	8	
+		5 •	4	
		•		
		•		

b) 16·75 + 1·83 = ☐

	T	O •	Tth	Hth
	1	6 •	7	5
+		1 •	8	3
		•		
		•		

c) 0·194 + 0·907 = ☐

	T	O •	Tth	Hth	Thths
		0 •	1	9	4
+		0 •	9	0	7
		•			
		•			

d) 13·8 + 26·4 = ☐

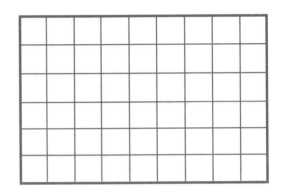

e) 4·76 + 3·2 = ☐

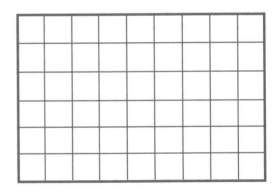

f) 126·9 + 38·45 = ☐

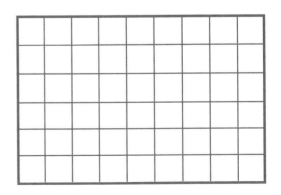

77

2 Toshi is working out 3·6 – 1·37.

He sets out the calculation like this.

		T	O	Tth	Hth
			3	0	6
–			1	3	7

Discuss with a partner the mistake Toshi has made.

3 Work out the subtractions.

a) 36·9 – 12·5

	T	O	Tth	Hth
	3	6	9	
–	1	2	5	

d) 6·18 – 1·7

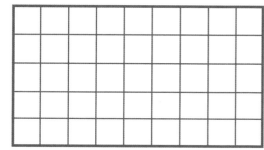

b) 6·84 – 1·68

	T	O	Tth	Hth
		6	8	4
–		1	6	8

e) 42·73 – 23·05

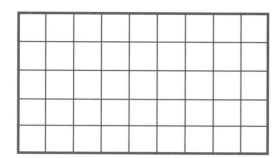

c) 0·729 – 0·052

		T	O	Tth	Hth	Thth
			0	7	2	9
–			0	0	5	2

f) 13·5 – 2·49

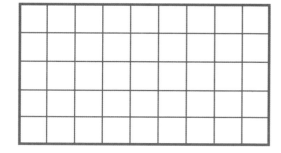

4 Complete the number sentences.

a) $4 \cdot 7 - 1 \cdot 3 =$ ☐   b) $4 \cdot 7 - 1 \cdot 35 =$ ☐   c) $4 \cdot 7 - 1 \cdot 359 =$ ☐

5 Complete the number sentences.

CHALLENGE

a) $6 \cdot 3 +$ ☐ $= 11 \cdot 18$

b) $9 \cdot 5 -$ ☐ $= 3 \cdot 08$

Reflect

Why is it important to make sure you set our your calculation correctly?

_____

_____

Date: _____

Multiply by 10, 100 and 1,000

1 Use the place value grids to multiply each number by 10.

a) $1·75 \times 10 =$ ⬚

T	O	Tth	Hth	Tth
	1	7	5	

b) $3·8 \times 10 =$ ⬚

T	O	Tth	Hth	Tth
	3	8		

c) $2·095 \times 10 =$ ⬚

T	O	Tth	Hth	Tth
	2	0	9	5

d) $26·3 \times 10 =$ ⬚

T	O	Tth	Hth	Tth
2	6	3		

2 Use the place value grids to multiply each number by 100.

a) 3·48

T	O	Tth	Hth	Tth
	3	4	8	

b) 0·19

T	O	Tth	Hth	Tth
		1	9	

c) 5·7

T	O	Tth	Hth	Tth
	5	7		

d) 0·045

T	O	Tth	Hth	Tth
			4	5

3 Use the place value grids to multiply each number by 1,000.

a) 1·9

T	O	Tth	Hth	Tth
	1	9		

c) 0·711

T	O	Tth	Hth	Tth
		7	1	1

b) 1·95

T	O	Tth	Hth	Tth
	1	9	5	

d) 0·038

T	O	Tth	Hth	Tth
			3	8

4 Bella multiplies 1·6 by 100.

The answer is 1·600.

Bella

a) What mistake has Bella made?

_____

_____

b) What is the correct answer? ☐

5 Complete the table.

Number	× 10	× 100	× 1,000
1·2	12	120	1,200
3·8			
4·59			
13·7			

6 Find the missing numbers.

a) $1\cdot5 \times \boxed{} = 15$

b) $6\cdot03 \times \boxed{} = 603$

c) $6\cdot8 \times \boxed{} = 6{,}800$

d) $\boxed{} \times 100 = 25\cdot8$

e) $1\cdot76 \times \boxed{} = 17\cdot6$

f) $\boxed{} \times 100 = 3$

g) $1\cdot7 \times 10 \times 10 = 1\cdot7 \times \boxed{}$

h) $3\cdot85 \times 10 \times 10 \times 10 = 3\cdot85 \times \boxed{}$

---

7 $0\cdot004 \times \blacktriangle = \bigstar \times 0\cdot04$

CHALLENGE

How many different solutions can you find?

	Solution 1	Solution 2	Solution 3	Solution 4	Solution 5	Solution 6	Solution 7
▲							
★							

Reflect

When multiplying decimals by 10, 100 and 1,000, I will _____

_____

_____

Divide by 10, 100 and 1,000

↓ Textbook 6B p112

1 Divide each number by 10.

a) 26·3

H	T	O	• Tth	Hth	Tth
	2	6	• 3		
			•		

[ ]

b) 4·5

H	T	O	• Tth	Hth	Tth
		4	• 5		
			•		

[ ]

c) 28

H	T	O	• Tth	Hth	Tth
		2	8 •		
			•		

[ ]

d) 176

H	T	O	• Tth	Hth	Tth
	1	7	6 •		
			•		

[ ]

2 Divide each number by 100.

a) 139

H	T	O	• Tth	Hth	Tth
	1	3	9 •		
			•		

[ ]

b) 26·4

H	T	O	• Tth	Hth	Tth
	2	6	• 4		
			•		

[ ]

c) 1·8

H	T	O	• Tth	Hth	Tth
			1 • 8		
			•		

[ ]

d) 3

H	T	O	• Tth	Hth	Tth
		3	•		
			•		

[ ]

3 Divide each number by 1,000.

a) 2,700

TTh	Th	H	T	O	Tth	Hth
	2	7	0	0		

b) 169

TTh	Th	H	T	O	Tth	Hth
		1	6	9		

4 Complete the table.

Number	÷ 10	÷ 100	÷ 1,000
13	1·3	0·13	0·013
140			
2,018			

5 Solve the divisions.

a) $21·9 \div 10 =$

b) $184 \div 100 =$

c) $175 \div 10 =$

d) $7,600 \div 1,000 =$

e) $0·59 \div 10 =$

6 Complete the number sentences.

a) $18 \div \boxed{} = 1.8$

c) $39 \div \boxed{} = 0.039$

b) $2 \div \boxed{} = 0.02$

d) $\boxed{} \div 10 = 0.19$

7 Join the numbers to make six accurate divisions.

Write each division out in full. One has been done for you.

CHALLENGE

206	÷ 10	2·6	$\longrightarrow$	$206 \div 1{,}000 = 0.206$
26	÷ 100	0·206	$\longrightarrow$	_____
260	÷ 1,000	0·206	$\longrightarrow$	_____
20·6	÷ 10	0·026	$\longrightarrow$	_____
2·6	÷ 100	0·026	$\longrightarrow$	_____
2·06	÷ 1,000	2·06	$\longrightarrow$	_____

Reflect

Dividing by 100 is the same as dividing by 10 and then 10 again.

Is this statement true or false? Give reasons and an example for your answer.

_____

_____

_____

Date: _____

Multiply decimals by integers

1 Complete these multiplication calculations.

a)

O	Tth	Hth
	0·1 0·1 0·1 0·1 0·1 0·1 0·1 0·1	

$2 \times 0.4 = \boxed{}$

b)

O	Tth	Hth
		0·01 0·01 0·01 0·01 0·01 0·01

$3 \times 0.02 = \boxed{}$

c)

O	Tth	Hth
	0·1 0·1 0·1 0·1 0·1 0·1 0·1 0·1 0·1 0·1 0·1 0·1 0·1 0·1 0·1	

$0.3 \times 5 = \boxed{}$

2 Complete the number sentences.

a) $0.4 \times 2 = \boxed{}$

$0.4 \times 3 = \boxed{}$

$0.4 \times 4 = \boxed{}$

$0.4 \times 5 = \boxed{}$

$7 \times 0.4 = \boxed{}$

b) $7 \times 3 = \boxed{}$

$0.7 \times 3 = \boxed{}$

$0.07 \times 3 = \boxed{}$

$0.007 \times 3 = \boxed{}$

c) Discuss with a partner what patterns you notice and how you worked out the answers.

3 Complete the calculations.

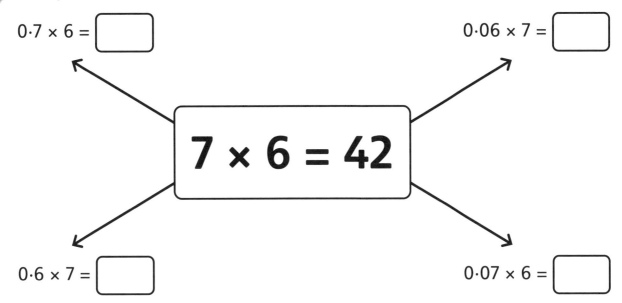

$0.7 \times 6 = \boxed{}$

$0.06 \times 7 = \boxed{}$

$7 \times 6 = 42$

$0.6 \times 7 = \boxed{}$

$0.07 \times 6 = \boxed{}$

4 Do you agree? Explain your reasoning.

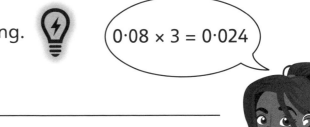

$0.08 \times 3 = 0.024$

_____

_____

_____

5 Work out the missing numbers.

Use the multiplication facts you know to help you.

a) $0.7 \times 2 = \boxed{}$

b) $6 \times 0.8 = \boxed{}$

c) $0.03 \times 3 = \boxed{}$

d) $0.002 \times 4 = \boxed{}$

e) $\boxed{} \times 7 = 3.5$

f) $0.02 \times \boxed{} = 0.06$

g) $0.02 \times \boxed{} = 0.16$

h) $6 \times \boxed{} = 2.4$

i) $6 \times \boxed{} = 0.24$

j) $6 \times \boxed{} = 0.024$

6 **a)** Work out 17 × 8 and 219 × 3.

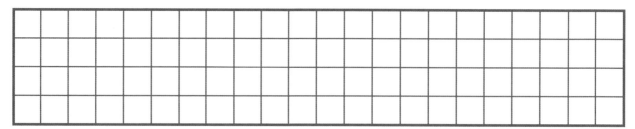

b) Use your answers to part a) to complete these multiplications.

17 × 0·8 = ⬜

17 × 0·08 = ⬜

219 × 0·3 = ⬜

219 × 0·03 = ⬜

7 These rectangles have the same area.

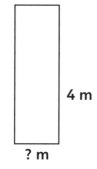

3 m

4 m

0·8 m

? m

What is the length of the missing side?

Show your working.

Reflect

Discuss with a partner how you can use known facts to work out 0·4 × 7.

Divide decimals by integers

1 Complete the divisions.

a) $14 \div 2 = \boxed{}$

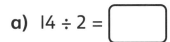

b) $1.4 \div 2 = \boxed{}$

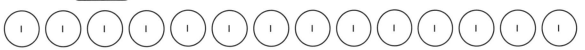

c) $0.14 \div 2 = \boxed{}$

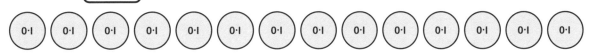

d) What patterns do you notice?

_____

_____

2 Complete the divisions.

a)

0·1 0·1 0·1 0·1 0·1 0·1

$0.6 \div 3 = \boxed{}$

b)

0·1 0·1 0·1 0·1 0·1 0·1 0·1 0·1 0·1 0·1 0·1 0·1

$1.2 \div 6 = \boxed{}$

c)

0·01 0·01 0·01 0·01 0·01 0·01 0·01 0·01

$\boxed{} \div 4 = \boxed{}$

3 **a)** Complete these division calculations.

36 ÷ 4 = ☐   48 ÷ 4 = ☐   16 ÷ 4 = ☐

3·6 ÷ 4 = ☐   4·8 ÷ 4 = ☐   1·6 ÷ 4 = ☐

0·36 ÷ 4 = ☐   0·48 ÷ 4 = ☐   0·16 ÷ 4 = ☐

b) Complete these division calculations.

3·6 ÷ 6 = ☐   4·8 ÷ 6 = ☐

0·72 ÷ 6 = ☐   0·18 ÷ 6 = ☐

4 Work out the missing numbers.

Use the multiplication facts you know to help you.

a) 2·4 ÷ ☐ = 1·2   **f)** ☐ ÷ 4 = 0·7

b) 3·6 ÷ ☐ = 0·6   **g)** ☐ ÷ 7 = 0·07

c) 0·36 ÷ ☐ = 0·12   **h)** ☐ ÷ 2 = 0·12

d) 0·45 ÷ ☐ = 0·09   **i)** ☐ ÷ 3 = 0·4

e) 0·45 ÷ ☐ = 0·05   **j)** ☐ ÷ 5 = 0·005

5 6 boxes have a total mass of 4·2 kg.

What is the mass of 5 boxes?

Show all the steps in your working out.

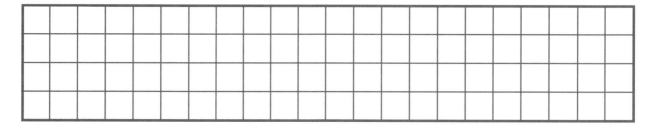

6 Complete the divisions.

a) $8.64 \div 6 = $ ⬚

		.		
6	8	.	6	4

b) $9.2 \div 8 = $ ⬚

		.		
8	9	.	2	

7 Oliver makes 0·2 using counters.

O	•	Tth	Hth
	•	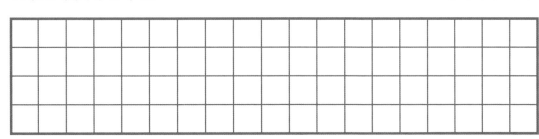	

Oliver wants to divide his number by 5.

Discuss with a partner how he can do this.

Work out 0·2 ÷ 5.

I will use counters to help me.

Reflect

Explain the mistake.

$0.24 \div 6 = 0.4$

_____

_____

Date: _____

Fractions to decimals

 1 Match each fraction to its decimal equivalent.

$\frac{1}{4}$		0·75

$\frac{1}{2}$		0·25

$\frac{3}{4}$		1

$\frac{4}{4}$		0·5

 2 Lexi makes the fraction $\frac{2}{10}$ using counters.

T	O	•	Tth
			○○

a) What is Lexi's fraction as a decimal?

b) Write each fraction as a decimal.

$\frac{1}{10} = \boxed{}$ $\frac{3}{10} = \boxed{}$

$\frac{7}{10} = \boxed{}$ $\frac{9}{10} = \boxed{}$

3 Use the fraction wall to help convert these fractions to decimals.

| $\frac{1}{5}$ | $\frac{1}{5}$ | $\frac{1}{5}$ | $\frac{1}{5}$ | $\frac{1}{5}$ |

$\frac{1}{10}$ $\frac{1}{10}$ $\frac{1}{10}$ $\frac{1}{10}$ $\frac{1}{10}$ $\frac{1}{10}$ $\frac{1}{10}$ $\frac{1}{10}$ $\frac{1}{10}$ $\frac{1}{10}$

$\frac{1}{20}$ $\frac{1}{20}$ $\frac{1}{20}$ $\frac{1}{20}$ $\frac{1}{20}$ $\frac{1}{20}$ $\frac{1}{20}$ $\frac{1}{20}$ $\frac{1}{20}$ $\frac{1}{20}$ $\frac{1}{20}$ $\frac{1}{20}$ $\frac{1}{20}$ $\frac{1}{20}$ $\frac{1}{20}$ $\frac{1}{20}$ $\frac{1}{20}$ $\frac{1}{20}$ $\frac{1}{20}$ $\frac{1}{20}$

0   0·1   0·2   0·3   0·4   0·5   0·6   0·7   0·8   0·9   1

a) $\frac{2}{5}$ = ☐

b) $\frac{8}{20}$ = ☐

c) $\frac{14}{20}$ = ☐

d) $\frac{4}{5}$ = ☐

e) $\frac{11}{20}$ = ☐

f) $\frac{17}{20}$ = ☐

4 Complete the table of equivalent fractions and decimals.

Fraction	$\frac{7}{100}$	$\frac{12}{100}$	$\frac{38}{100}$		
Decimal				0·79	0·02

5 Use equivalent fractions to convert these fractions to decimals.

a) $\frac{1}{50} = \frac{☐}{100} = 0·☐$

b) $\frac{3}{50} = \frac{☐}{100} = ☐$

c) $\frac{3}{200} = \frac{☐}{1,000} = ☐$

d) $\frac{99}{500} = \frac{☐}{☐} = ☐$

6 Convince a partner that $\frac{3}{12}$ is the same as 0·25.

7 **a)** Convert these fractions to decimals.

$\dfrac{4}{5}$ $\dfrac{7}{10}$ $\dfrac{77}{100}$

[ ]   [ ]   [ ]

b) Use your answer to part a) to put the fractions in order from smallest to greatest.

[ ]   [ ]   [ ]

8 Max says, '0·28 of this grid is shaded.'

Is Max correct?

Explain your answer.

CHALLENGE

_____

_____

_____

Reflect

Test a partner on common fraction and decimal equivalents.

Check that they know their fifths, tenths and quarters.

Fractions as division

1 Match each fraction to its decimal equivalent.

$\frac{1}{8}$

$\frac{1}{5}$

$\frac{1}{10}$

0·1

0·125

0·2

2 Aisha converts $\frac{5}{6}$ to a decimal using division.

	1	·	2	
5	6	·	¹0	

a) What mistake has Aisha made?

_____

_____

b) Convert $\frac{5}{6}$ to a decimal.

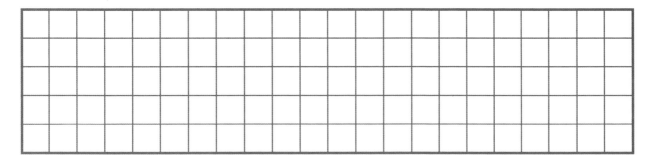

c) Why do you think $\frac{5}{6}$ is known as a recurring decimal? Discuss with a partner.

95

3 **a)** Use short division to show that $\frac{3}{4}$ is equal to 0·75.

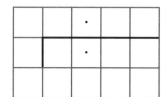

b) Convert these fractions to decimals using short division.

$\frac{5}{8} = \boxed{}$

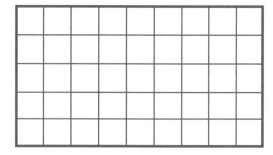

$\frac{12}{5} = \boxed{}$

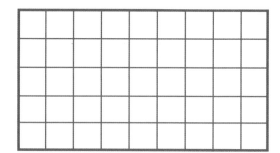

4 Convert these fractions into decimals. Give your answers to three decimal places.

a) $\frac{7}{8}$

c) $\frac{2}{7}$

b) $\frac{5}{12}$

d) $\frac{14}{15}$

5 **a)** Use short division to find the decimal equivalents of these fractions.

 CHALLENGE

$\frac{1}{9} = 1 \div 9$

	0	.			
9	1	.	¹0		

$\frac{2}{9} = 2 \div 9$

	0	.			
9	2	.	²0		

$\frac{3}{9} = \boxed{} \div \boxed{}$

$\frac{4}{9} = \boxed{} \div \boxed{}$

b) Without working them out, predict the missing decimal equivalents to three decimal places.

$\frac{5}{9} = 0 \cdot \boxed{}$

$\frac{9}{9} = \boxed{}$

$\frac{6}{9} = 0 \cdot \boxed{}$

$\frac{10}{9} = \boxed{}$

$\frac{7}{9} = 0 \cdot \boxed{}$

$\frac{11}{9} = \boxed{}$

$\frac{8}{9} = 0 \cdot \boxed{}$

$\frac{19}{9} = \boxed{}$

Reflect

Discuss with a partner what you have learned about fractions as division.

Date: _____

End of unit check

My journal

→ Textbook 6B p132

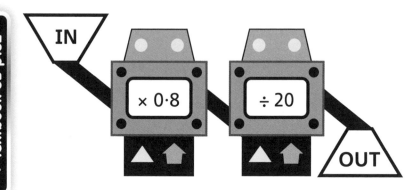

Try each of these inputs in the function machine.

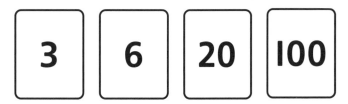

| 3 | 6 | 20 | 100 |

What are the outputs?

Show your working and explain any patterns you notice.

Power check

How do you feel about your work in this unit?

Power play

With a partner, take it in turns to use the spinner or roll a dice to get three digits.

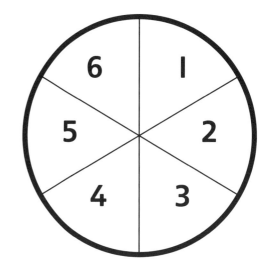

Choose how to use the digits to complete this multiplication, and then calculate the answer.

☐.☐ × ☐

Mark your number on this number line with your initials.

The winner is the first person to get three numbers in a row on the number line, without their partner getting any of the numbers in between.

You can play this game with different calculations. For example,

or

99

Date: _____

Understand percentages

1 What percentage is shown on each 100 grid?

a)

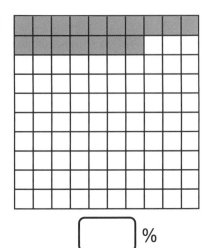

☐ %

c)

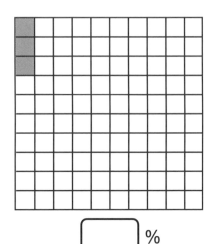

☐ %

b)

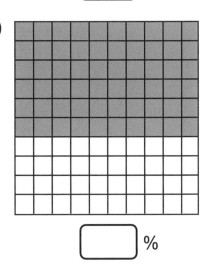

☐ %

d)

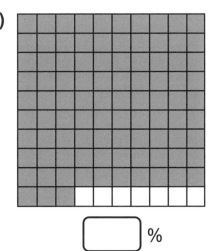

☐ %

2 Shade in these percentages on the 100 grids.

a) 40%

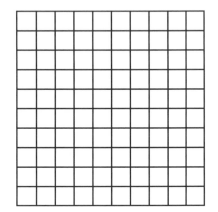

b) 15%

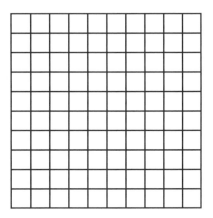

3 Here is a 100 grid.

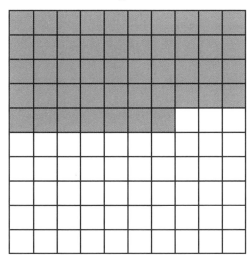

a) What percentage of the 100 grid is already shaded? ⬜ %

b) Shade in 15% of the 100 grid in one colour.

c) Shade in 21% of the 100 grid in a different colour.

d) What percentage of the 100 grid is not shaded? ⬜ %

4 Here is a 100 square.

1	2	3	4	5	6	7	8	9	10
11	12	13	14	15	16	17	18	19	20
21	22	23	24	25	26	27	28	29	30
31	32	33	34	35	36	37	38	39	40
41	42	43	44	45	46	47	48	49	50
51	52	53	54	55	56	57	58	59	60
61	62	63	64	65	66	67	68	69	70
71	72	73	74	75	76	77	78	79	80
81	82	83	84	85	86	87	88	89	90
91	92	93	94	95	96	97	98	99	100

a) What percentage of the numbers are even? ⬜ %

b) What percentage of the 100 square contains multiples of 5? ⬜

c) What percentage of the 100 square contains the digit 1? ⬜

d) What percentage of the 100 square are square numbers? ⬜

101

5   Lexi gets 36 marks out of 100 in a test.

What percentage did she get? ⬚

Discuss your answer with a partner.

CHALLENGE

6   a)   What percentage of this grid is shaded?

⬚ % is shaded.

b)   Shade in another 20% of the grid.

c)   Is it possible to shade 5% of the grid?

Discuss with a partner.

_____

_____

_____

Reflect

Percentages are always out of 100. Discuss this statement with a partner.

- _____
- _____
- _____

Fractions to percentages

→ Textbook 6B p140

1 Write each fraction as a percentage.

Use the 100 grids to help you.

a)

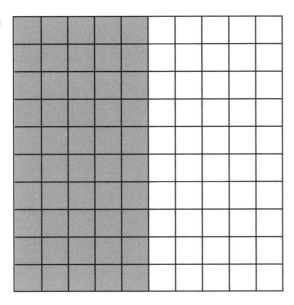

$\frac{1}{2} = \boxed{} \%$

c)

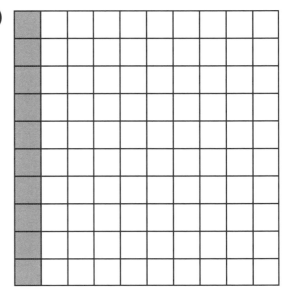

$\frac{1}{10} = \boxed{} \%$

b)

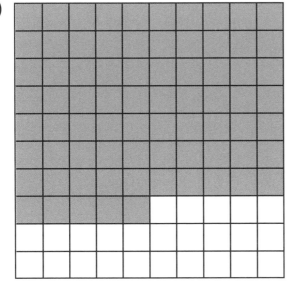

$\frac{3}{4} = \boxed{} \%$

d)

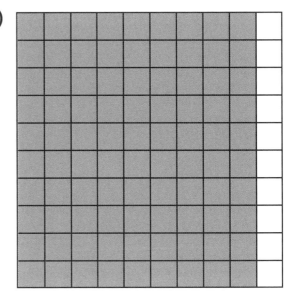

$\frac{9}{10} = \boxed{} \%$

2 Write each fraction as a percentage.

a) $\dfrac{2}{10} = \boxed{}$ %

$\dfrac{7}{10} = \boxed{}$ %

$\dfrac{8}{10} = \boxed{}$ %

b) $\dfrac{1}{5} = \boxed{}$ %

$\dfrac{2}{5} = \boxed{}$ %

$\dfrac{3}{5} = \boxed{}$ %

$\dfrac{4}{5} = \boxed{}$ %

3 Write each fraction out of 100, then convert each fraction to a percentage.

a) $\dfrac{11}{50} = \dfrac{\boxed{}}{100} = \boxed{}$ %

b) $\dfrac{17}{50} = \dfrac{\boxed{}}{100} = \boxed{}$ %

c) $\dfrac{12}{25} = \dfrac{\boxed{}}{100} = \boxed{}$ %

d) $\dfrac{9}{25} = \dfrac{\boxed{}}{100} = \boxed{}$ %

e) $\dfrac{11}{20} = \dfrac{\boxed{}}{100} = \boxed{}$ %

f) $\dfrac{84}{200} = \dfrac{\boxed{}}{100} = \boxed{}$ %

4 What percentage of each grid is shaded?

a) 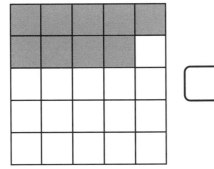 [ ] %

b) 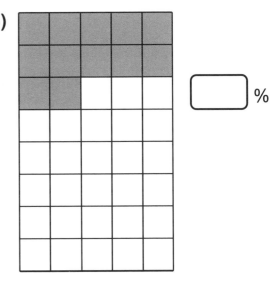 [ ] %

5 Max gets 24 out of 40 in a maths test.

What percentage did he get?

CHALLENGE

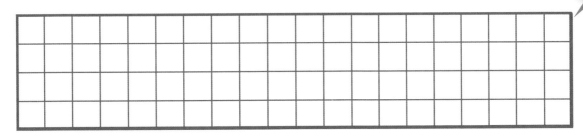

Reflect

Explain how to convert a fraction to a percentage.

Date: _____

Equivalent fractions, decimals and percentages

Textbook 6B p144

1 Complete the equivalent decimals, fractions and percentages for this number line.

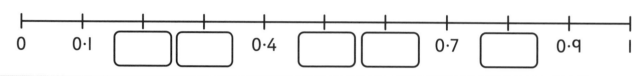

2 Write the fraction, decimal and percentage represented in each diagram.

a)

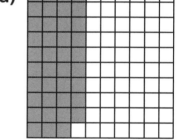

b)

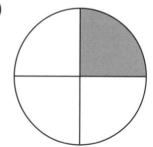

c)

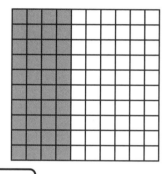

d)

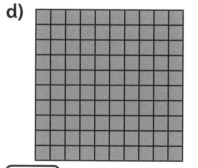

3 Match the equivalent amounts.

| $\frac{17}{100}$ | $\frac{7}{100}$ | 70% | 71% |

| 0·07 | 0·71 | 0·17 | 0·7 |

4 **a)** Write each fraction as a percentage and then as a decimal.

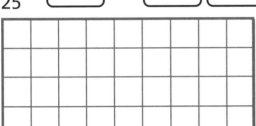

$\frac{11}{25} = \boxed{}\% = \boxed{}\cdot\boxed{}$

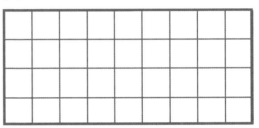

$\frac{39}{50} = \boxed{}\% = \boxed{}\cdot\boxed{}$

b) Write each percentage as a fraction and then as a decimal.

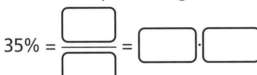

$35\% = \frac{\boxed{}}{\boxed{}} = \boxed{}\cdot\boxed{}$

$96\% = \frac{\boxed{}}{\boxed{}} = \boxed{}\cdot\boxed{}$

5 Complete the table.

Percentage	Decimal	Fraction
66%		
	0·6	
		$\frac{9}{100}$
	0·9	

107

6 Jamie says that to convert a decimal to a percentage, all you have to do is remove the '0·' and add '%' to the end. For example, 0·43 = 43%.

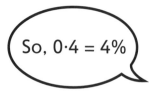

So, 0·4 = 4%

and 0·125 = 125%.

Jamie

Explain Jamie's mistakes.

_____

_____

_____

_____

Reflect

Estimate the fraction, decimal and percentage shown by this bar.

- _____
- _____
- _____

Order fractions, decimals and percentages

1 In each pair, circle the greater amount.

a) $\frac{73}{100}$ 75%

c) 0·79   75%

b) $\frac{7}{10}$ 75%

d) 78% $\frac{3}{4}$

2 a) Write $\frac{27}{50}$ as a percentage. ☐ %

b) Which is greater, $\frac{27}{50}$ or 48%?

Explain your answer.

_____

_____

3 In each pair, circle the smaller amount.

a) 18%   0·22

c) 18%   0·3

b) 18% $\frac{3}{20}$

d) 18% $\frac{13}{100}$

4 **a)** Write each number as a percentage.

$\frac{9}{20}$ $\frac{5}{25}$ 0·68

□ %   □ %   □ %

b) Put the numbers in order from smallest to largest.

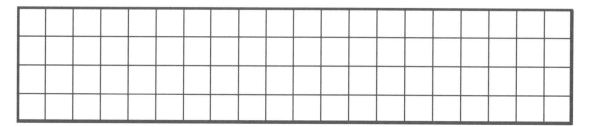

5 Fill in the blanks with a < or > sign.

a) $\frac{4}{5}$ ◯ 85%

c) 99% ◯ $\frac{180}{200}$

b) $\frac{3}{10}$ ◯ 45%

d) 0·44 ◯ $\frac{18}{50}$

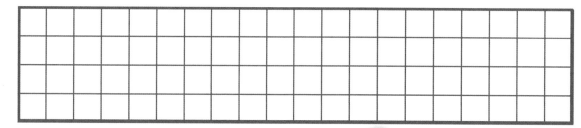

6 Is 1·8 more than 1$\frac{17}{20}$? Explain your answer.

7 **a)** Ebo has eaten 87% of an apple. Lexi has eaten $\frac{4}{9}$ of 2 apples. Who has eaten the most apple?

CHALLENGE

Draw a diagram to show your reasoning.

_____ has eaten the most apple.

b) What assumptions did you have to make?

_____

_____

_____

Reflect

Explain how to order fractions, decimals and percentages.

To order fractions, decimals and percentages _____

_____

_____

_____

Date: _____

Simple percentage of an amount

 1

a) What is 10% of 40?

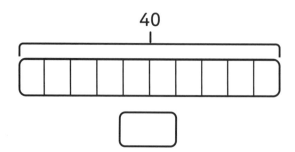

40

b) What is 20% of £240?

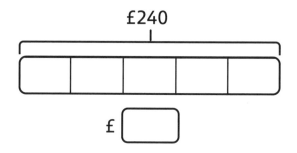

£240

£ [ ]

c) What is 25% of 300 metres?

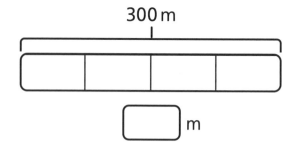

300 m

[ ] m

d) What is 50% of 700?

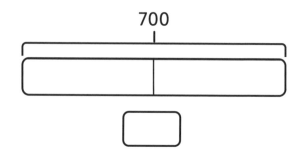

700

e) What is 10% of 90 kg?

f) What is 10% of £980?

2 Explain Zac's mistake. Draw diagrams to support your explanation.

> To find 10% of a number, I divide by 10. So, to find 20% of a number, I divide by 20.

Zac

_____

_____

3 Complete the table.

Starting number	10% of the number	20% of the number
400		
410		
41		
401		
	1·4	
		4·1

4 A football crowd is made up of 52,000 fans. 20% support the away team. How many fans support the away team?

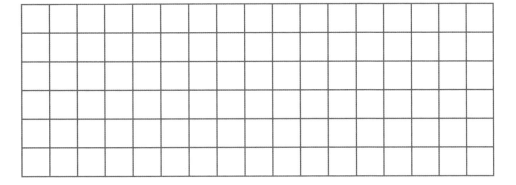

5 A chocolate bar weighs 400 g.

20% of the bar is cocoa and 25% is sugar.

a) How many more grams of sugar than cocoa are in the bar?

[ ] g

b) Andy eats 4 squares from the chocolate bar. How many grams of cocoa has he eaten?

[ ] g

Reflect

Lexi says that if she knows 10% of an amount, she can work out any other amount. Is she correct? Explain your answer.

Date: _____

Percentage of an amount – 1%

↓ Textbook 6B p156

1 Find 1% of each number.

a) 600 [　]   d) 1,700 [　]   g) 550 kg [　]

b) 700 [　]   e) 3,200 [　]   h) 60 [　]

c) 900 [　]   f) £26,000 [　]   i) £70 [　]

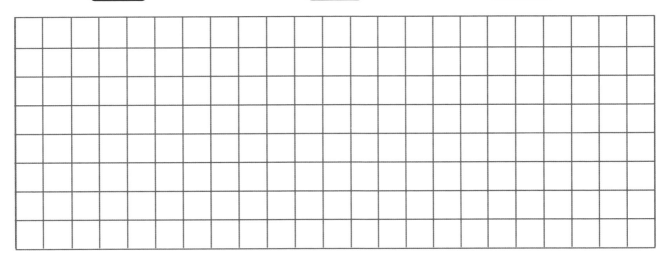

2 Match the calculations to the correct answers.

1% of 300 = [　]

10% of 3,000 = [　]

1% of 30 = [　]

10% of 300 = [　]

0·3

3

30

300

3 Amelia has a jar of 1,200 marbles. 1% are Green Goblins and 3% are Sapphire Specials.

How many of each type are there?

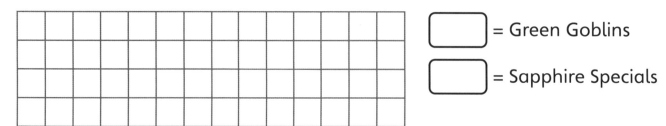

☐ = Green Goblins

☐ = Sapphire Specials

4 Complete the percentages.

a) 100% is £1,500.

   1% is £ ☐.

   2% is £ ☐.

   3% is £ ☐.

b) 100% is 150 m.

   1% is ☐ m.

   2% is ☐ m.

   3% is ☐ m.

c) 100% is 15 kg.

   1% is ☐ g.

   3% is ☐ g.

   6% is ☐ g.

5 Work out the percentages.

a) 2% of 600 km = ☐

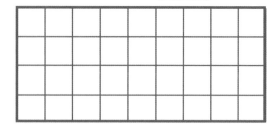

c) 3% of £250 = ☐

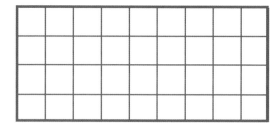

b) 10% of 56 cm = ☐

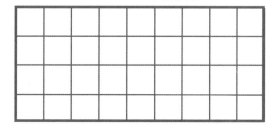

d) 25% of 18 = ☐

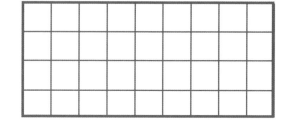

6 **a)** Do you agree with Reena? Explain your answer.

CHALLENGE

Reena

I think 3% of 200 must be equal to 2% of 300.

_____

_____

_____

b) Explore other examples like this. Explain what you notice and write a statement of your own.

_____

_____

_____

Reflect

Draw a diagram and explain how to find 3% of any number.

_____

_____

_____

_____

_____

Date: _____

Percentages of an amount

1 Calculate these percentages.

a) 30% of £400 = £ ⬚

£400

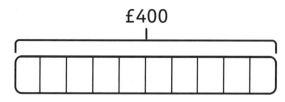

400 ÷ 10 = ⬚

⬚ × 3 = ⬚

b) 60% of 400 g = ⬚ g

c) 75% of £60 = £ ⬚

d) 15% of £120 = £ ⬚

2 Toshi plants 240 tulip bulbs. 10% are red tulips and 5% are yellow. The rest are pink. How many of each colour are there?

⬚ red ⬚ yellow and ⬚ pink tulips.

118

3 a) Complete these percentages.

50% of 700 = ☐   10% of 700 = ☐   1% of 700 = ☐

b) Now find these percentages of 700.

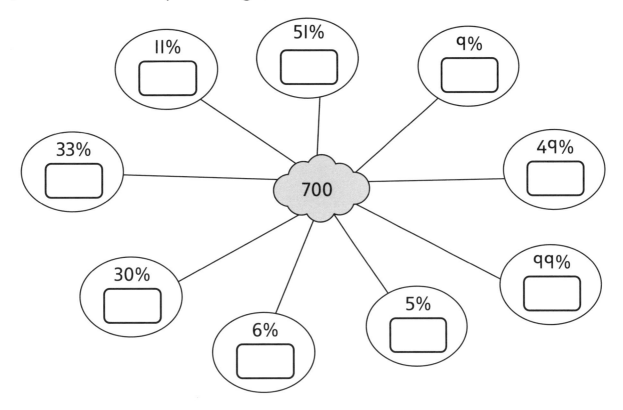

4 32,500 people signed up to run a marathon.

11% dropped out before race day. 29% did not complete the course.

How many people finished the marathon?

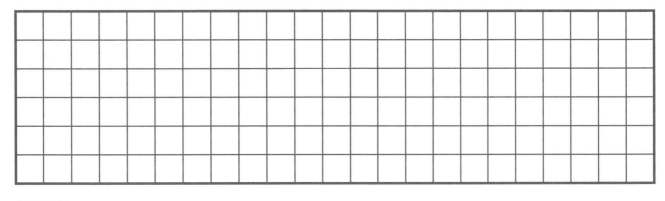

☐

5 On Monday, the groundskeeper mowed 30% of the football pitch.

On Tuesday, she mowed half of the remaining area.

On Wednesday, she mowed 1,250 square metres.

What area of the pitch was left to mow on Thursday?

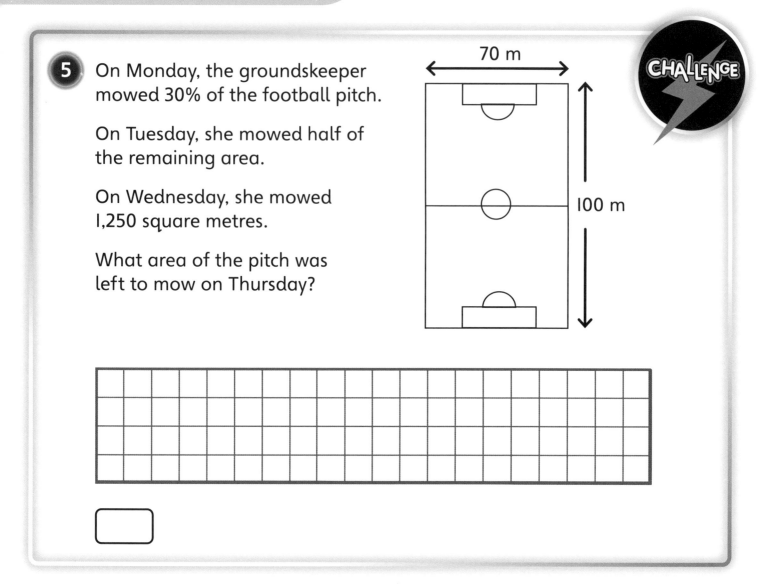

Reflect

Show two different ways to find 85% of 300.

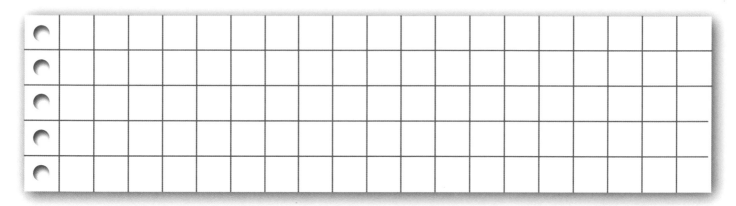

Percentages (missing values)

1 Fill in the missing values.

a) 50% of [ ] = 38

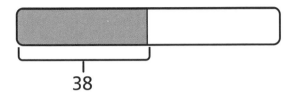

38

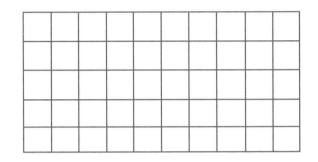

b) 25% of [ ] = 16

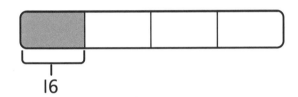

16

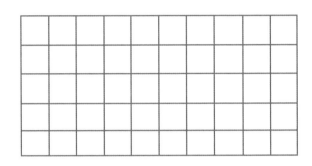

c) 10% of [ ] = 1·5

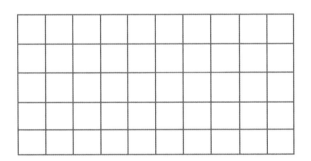

2 Match each calculation to the correct bar model. Then solve it.

40% of 60 = [ ]   40% of [ ] = 60

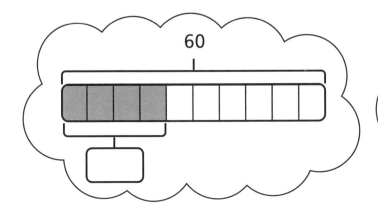

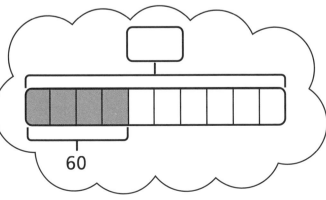

3 **a)** In a bag of orange and lemon sweets, 30% are orange and 63 sweets are lemon. How many orange sweets are there?

orange   lemon

b) Amelia has a piece of string. She cuts off 25%. The piece that is left is 240 cm long. How long was the string before she cut it?

cm

4 Find a solution to Aki's percentage puzzle.

I am thinking of a number. I subtract 20. I then find 10% of what is left. I finish on 40. What number did I start with?

Aki

5 Complete these calculations.

a) 10% of ☐ = 9

20% of ☐ = 9

30% of ☐ = 9

b) 30% of ☐ = 90

30% of ☐ = 180

30% of ☐ = 1,800

6 15% of the whole rectangle is shaded. What is the perimeter of the whole rectangle?

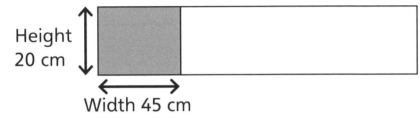

Height 20 cm

Width 45 cm

☐ cm

Reflect

Draw diagrams to show the differences between '20% of 45 = ?' and '20% of ? = 45'.

Date: _____

End of unit check

My journal

↑ Textbook 6B p168

1 **a)** Shade in 25% of the diagram. Explain your decisions.

b) Shade in 35% of this diagram.

Power check

How do you feel about your work in this unit?

Power play

- Play in pairs with two different sets of counters.

- Take it in turns to choose a problem to solve (for example, 10% of 900 = ?). If your answer is correct, place one of your counters on the square where the answer would go.

- The first person to get a full row of counters wins!

of	900		260		1
10%		17			
	9				
75%					
		170		25	
99%					

Try creating your own game and then swap with a partner.

125

Date: _____

Shapes – same area

1 Calculate the area of each rectangle. Do both the rectangles in each pair have the same area? Tick the correct box.

a) A

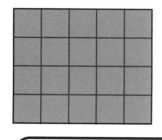

B

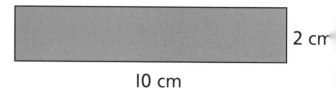

2 cm

10 cm

$\boxed{1 \text{ square} = 1 \text{ cm}^2}$

Area of rectangle A = $\boxed{}$ cm²

Area of rectangle B = $\boxed{}$ cm²

Rectangles A and B have the same area.

Yes $\square$ No $\square$

b) C

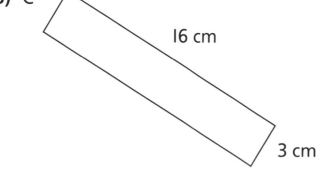

16 cm

3 cm

D   8 cm

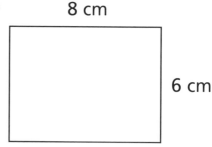

6 cm

Area of rectangle C = $\boxed{}$ cm²

Area of rectangle D = $\boxed{}$ cm²

Rectangles C and D have the same area.

Yes $\square$ No $\square$

Textbook 6B p172

a) Use these clues to draw three shapes that each have an area
of 36 cm².

	Shape A	Shape B	Shape C
Clue 1	Square	Rectangle	Compound shape
Clue 2		Length is 4 × width	

1 cm
↔

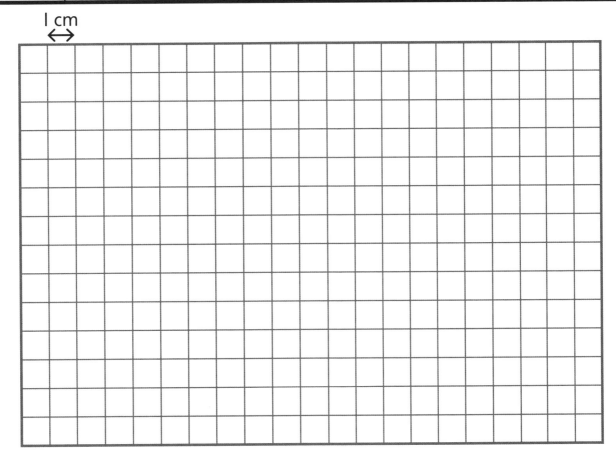

b) What other shapes with the same area can you draw?

3 All of these shapes have the same area. Calculate the missing measurements.

A

5 cm

6 cm

B

? cm

10 cm

[ ] cm

C

? cm

? cm

[ ] cm and [ ] cm

4 For a shape with this area, find all the values that L and W can be if they are whole numbers.

CHALLENGE

48 cm²

W cm

L cm

L cm					
W cm					

Reflect

Aki draws a plan of his room on squared paper. Every square represents 1 metre. His room is 4 m wide and 3 m long. How can Aki find the area of his room without counting every single square on the plan?

_____

_____

_____

Area and perimeter

↓ Textbook 6B p176

1 **a)** Complete the table.

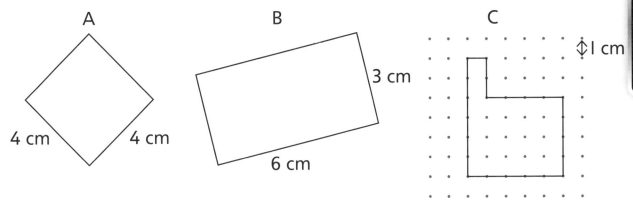

Shape	Area (cm²)	Perimeter (cm)
A		
B		
C		

b) What do shapes A, B and C have in common?

_____

_____

2 **a)** Draw a different shape with the same area as the shaded square.

b) Draw a different shape with the same perimeter as the shaded square.

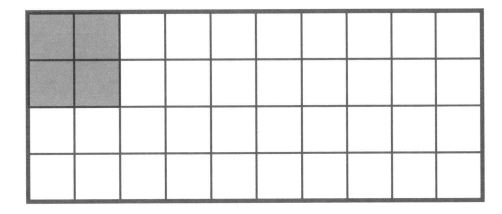

3 Complete the table. Which shapes have equal areas?

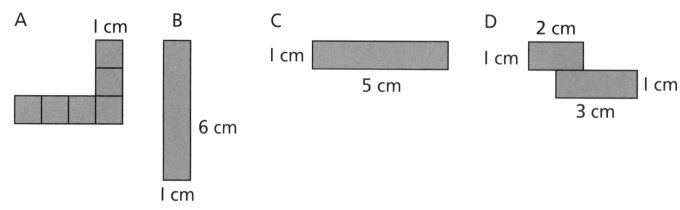

Shape	Area (cm²)	Perimeter (cm)
A		
B		
C		
D		

The shapes with equal areas are: _____

4 What do you notice about the areas and perimeters of these shapes? What is the same? What is different?

A

10 cm
2 cm

B

5 cm
4 cm

C

20 cm
1 cm

_____

_____

_____

⑤

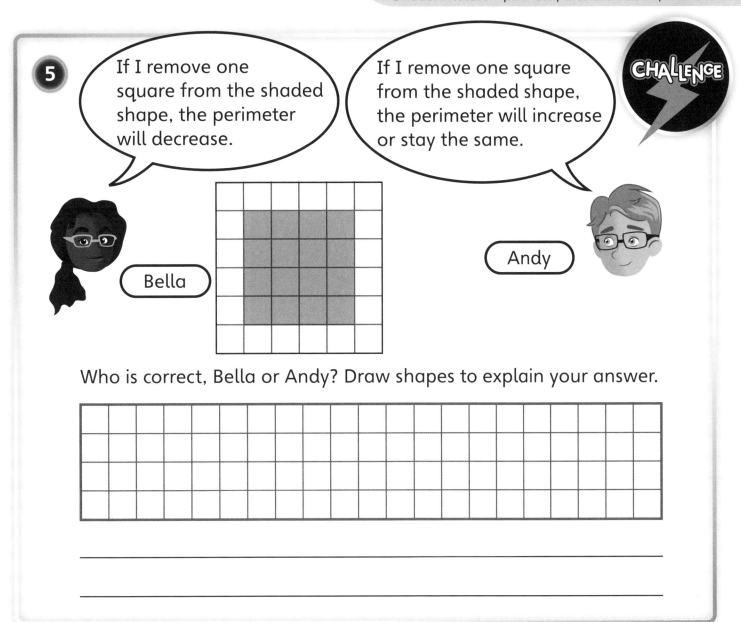

If I remove one square from the shaded shape, the perimeter will decrease.

Bella

If I remove one square from the shaded shape, the perimeter will increase or stay the same.

Andy

CHALLENGE

Who is correct, Bella or Andy? Draw shapes to explain your answer.

Reflect

Amy says: 'If two shapes have equal areas, their perimeters must be equal too.' Explain why Amy is not correct.

Date: _____

Area and perimeter – missing lengths

1 **a)** Complete the table.

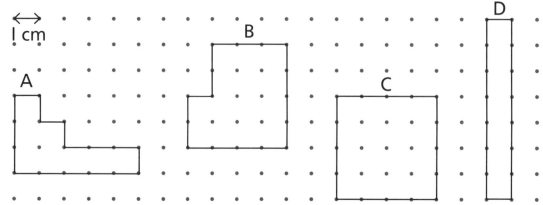

Shape	Area (cm²)	Perimeter (cm)
A		
B		
C		
D		

b) What do you notice about the shapes?

I notice that _____

_____.

2 Find the missing numbers. What do you notice about the numbers?

A   7 cm

? cm

Perimeter = 18 cm

Width = ☐ cm

Area = ☐ cm²

I notice that _____

B

? cm

3 cm

Perimeter = 18 cm

Length = ☐ cm

Area = ☐ cm²

_____.

3 Three shapes each have a perimeter of 12 cm. The area of shape A is 9 cm², the area of shape B is 5 cm² and the area of shape C is 8 cm².

Draw the three shapes.

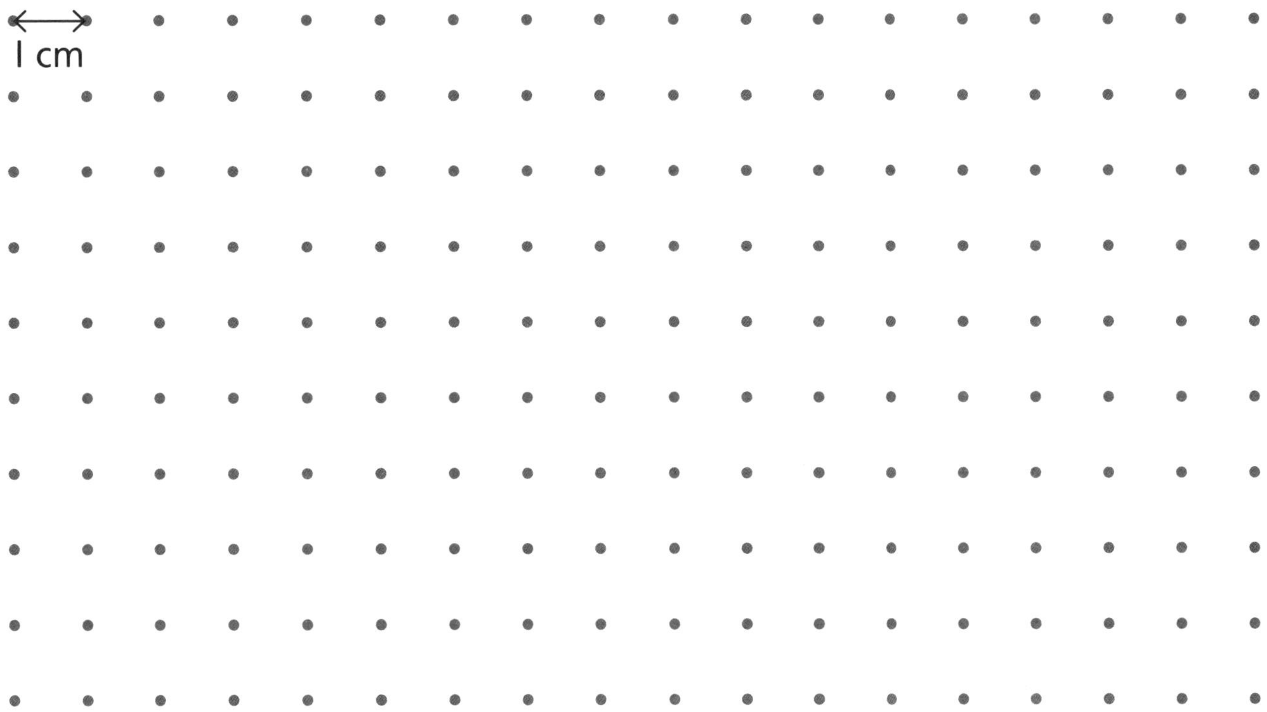

←—→
1 cm

4 Two gardens each have a perimeter of 30 m. The area of garden A is 4 times greater than the area of garden B. Work out the dimensions of each garden. Write them on the rectangles.

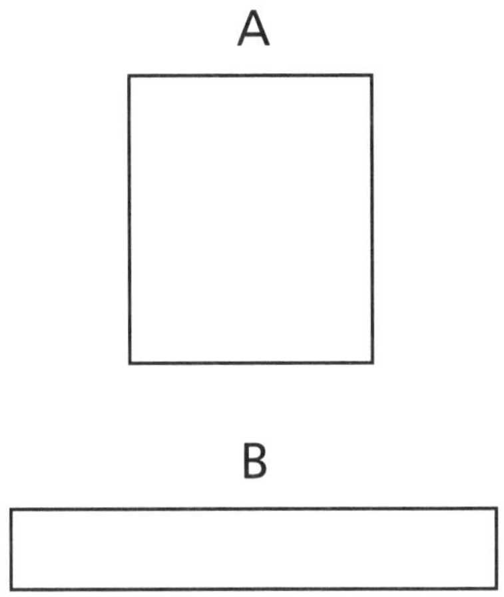

A

B

133

5 The shape below is made of square tiles. Which of the tiles can be removed without changing the perimeter?

_____

_____

_____

A	B	C	D	
	E	F	G	H
			I	

6 The perimeter of a rectangle is 18 cm. What is the greatest possible area of the rectangle? The lengths are all whole numbers.

CHALLENGE

The greatest possible area is _____ .

Reflect

Olivia says: 'Shapes with the same perimeter have the same area.' Use your knowledge from this lesson to say whether you agree or disagree with her.

_____

_____

_____

Area of a triangle – counting squares

1 Work out the area of each of the triangles.

Remember, the area of a rectangle = width × length.

I square = I cm^2

a)
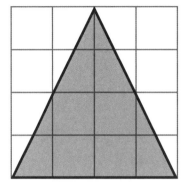

Area = ☐ cm^2

b)
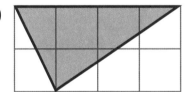

Area = ☐ cm^2

c)
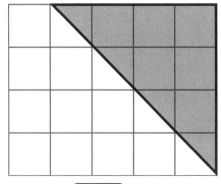

Area = ☐ cm^2

2 Estimate the area of each triangle by counting the squares.

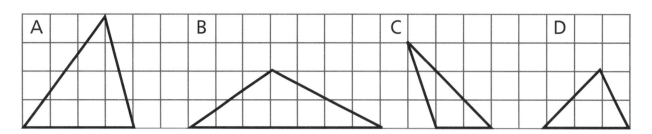

◻ cm²   ◻ cm²   ◻ cm²   ◻ cm²

3 Find the area of the triangle. Area = ◻ cm²

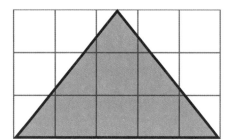

4 Draw a triangle that has an area as close to 20 cm² as possible.

a)

b) Measure the perimeter of your triangle.

5 Triangle A has an area of 6 cm². Jess thinks that the area of triangle B is twice the area of triangle A. Is she correct?

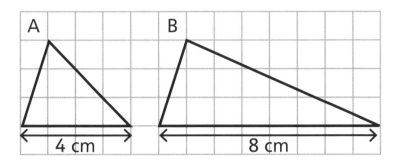

_____

_____

_____

_____

6 Find the area of the shape. Area = ☐ cm²

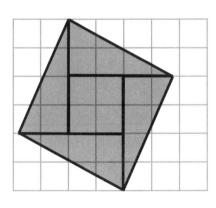

I square = I cm

Reflect

Describe the methods you used to find the area of the triangles in today's lesson.

_____

_____

_____

Date: _____

Area of a right-angled triangle

1 Find the area of each shaded right-angled triangle.

a)

6 cm

8 cm

Area = (⬚ × ⬚) ÷ 2

= ⬚ cm²

c)

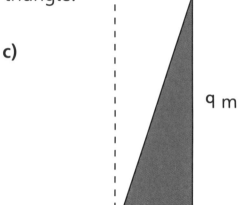

9 m

3 m

Area = (⬚ × ⬚) ÷ 2

= ⬚ m²

b)

5 cm

8 cm

Area = (⬚ × ⬚) ÷ 2

= ⬚ cm²

d)

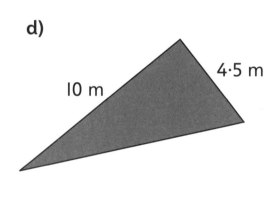

10 m

4·5 m

Area = (⬚ × ⬚) ÷ 2

= ⬚ m²

2 Danny thinks that the two triangles below have the same area.
Explain why Danny is wrong.

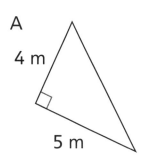

A
4 m
5 m

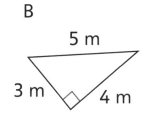

B
5 m
3 m
4 m

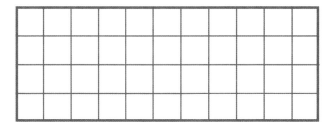

Look at the lengths carefully!

_____

_____

3 Look at the triangles below. Circle the triangle with the greatest area.

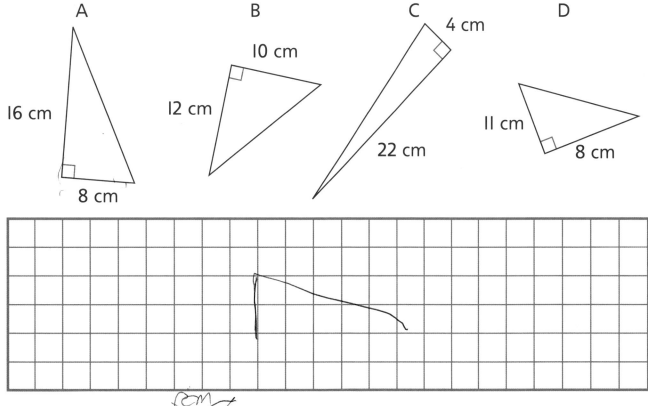

A
16 cm
8 cm

B
10 cm
12 cm

C
4 cm
22 cm

D
11 cm
8 cm

$3 \times 8 = \dfrac{24}{2} = 12$

139

4 Work out the area of the shaded triangle. Area = ☐ cm²

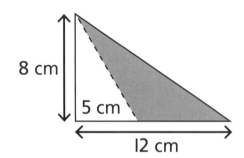 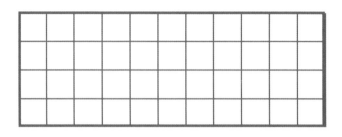

5 Richard cuts a triangle off the end of a rectangular strip of paper.

Calculate the area of paper left after Richard cuts off the triangle.

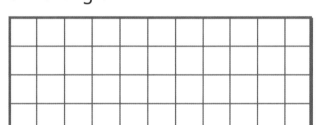 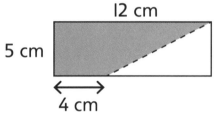

Area = ☐ cm²

Reflect

Explain how you can use the area of a rectangle to find the area of a right-angled triangle.

_____

_____

_____

Area of any triangle

① Find the area of each triangle below.   Not drawn to scale

A

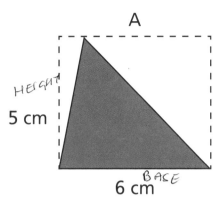

HEIGHT
5 cm

BASE
6 cm

B

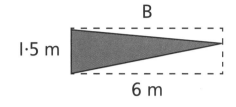

1·5 m

6 m

C

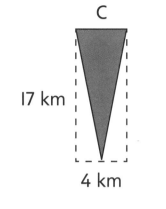

17 km

4 km

① Area of A = (5 × 6) ÷ 2 = 15 cm²

② Area of B = ($1·5$ × 6) ÷ 2 = $4·5$ m²

Area of C = (17 × 4) ÷ 2 = 34 km²

² $2D^2$

② Draw three different triangles with a base of 4 cm and an area of 8 cm².
What do the triangles have in common?

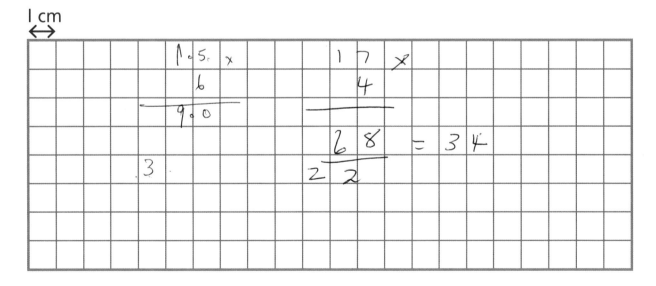

I cm
↔

_____

_____

3 **a)** Ben thinks that the area of this triangle is 24 cm². Explain what Ben has done wrong. What is the area of the triangle?

 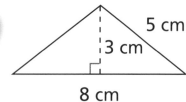

_____

_____

_____

b) Alex thinks that the area of this triangle is 60 cm². Is Alex correct? Explain why.

_____

_____

_____

4 Find the area of each triangle.

Not drawn to scale

a)

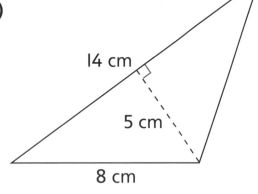

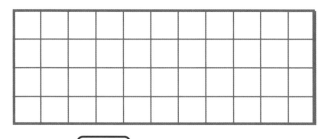

Area = [   ] cm².

b)

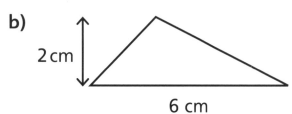

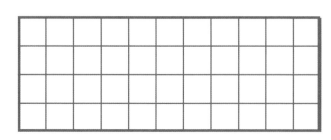

Area = [   ] cm².

5 **a)** Find the area of the shaded triangle. Area = ☐ cm².

CHALLENGE

40 cm

22 cm

40 cm

b) Draw your own square with three triangles inside and challenge a partner to find the area of one of the triangles. Make sure you give your partner enough measurements to work out the answer.

Reflect

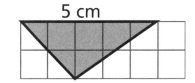

5 cm

Explain how to find the area of the shaded triangle.

_____

_____

Date: _____

Area of a parallelogram

1 Calculate the area of each parallelogram by changing it into a rectangle.

A

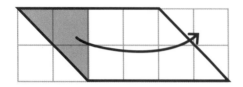

B

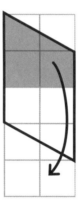

C

(I square = I cm)

Area of A = ⬚ cm × ⬚ cm = ⬚ cm²

Area of B = ⬚ cm × ⬚ cm = ⬚ cm²

Area of C = ⬚ cm × ⬚ cm = ⬚ cm²

2 Find the area of each parallelogram. Which of them is the odd one out?

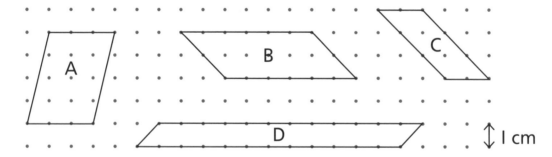

A = ⬚ × ⬚ = ⬚ cm²   C = ⬚ × ⬚ = ⬚ cm²

B = ⬚ × ⬚ = ⬚ cm²   D = ⬚ × ⬚ = ⬚ cm²

Parallelogram _____ is the odd one out because _____

_____ .

3 **a)** Find the area of each parallelogram.

A

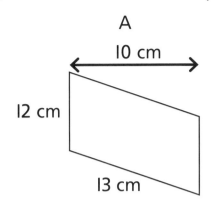

B

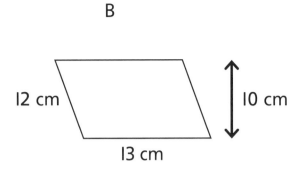

A = ⬚ × ⬚ = ⬚   B = ⬚ × ⬚ = ⬚

b) Use = or > or < to complete the sentence.

Area of parallelogram A ◯ area of parallelogram B.

4 Use the facts that are given in the diagrams to find lengths *a*, *b* and *c*.

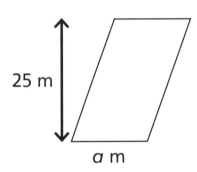

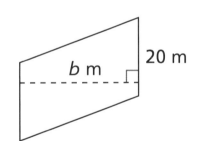

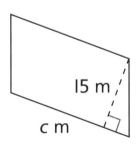

Area = 250 m²   Area = 500 m²   Area = 300 m²

a = ⬚ m   *b* = ⬚ m   *c* = ⬚ m

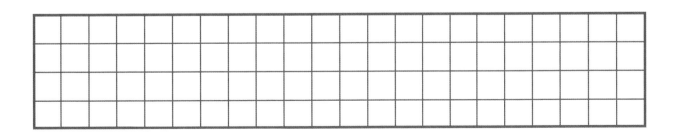

5 Explain how you know the areas of these parallelograms are the same.

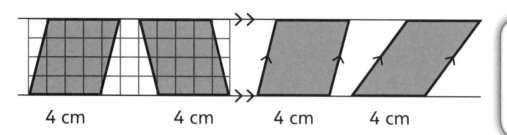

4 cm   4 cm   4 cm   4 cm

These arrow markings mean the lines are parallel.

_____

_____

_____

6 A path runs across a garden. What is the area of the path?

CHALLENGE

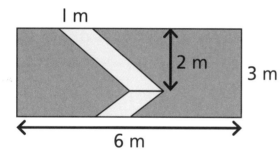

1 m

2 m

3 m

6 m

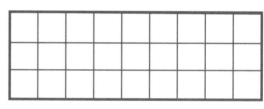

Area of the path = ☐ m²

Reflect

What is the area of the parallelogram?

a) 35 cm²   b) 42 cm²   c) 30 cm²

Give reasons for your choice.

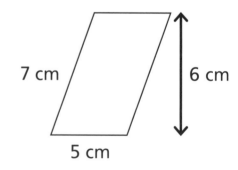

7 cm   6 cm

5 cm

_____

_____

Problem solving – area

1 Calculate the areas of the shapes below.

a)

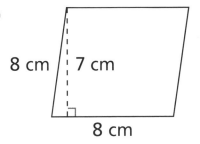

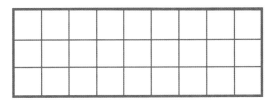

Area = ☐ cm²

b)

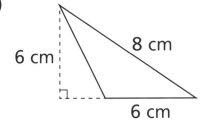

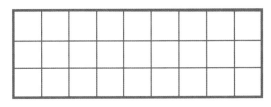

Area = ☐ cm²

c)

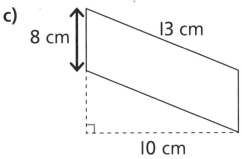

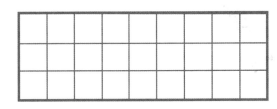

Area = ☐ cm²

2 These shapes have the same area.

Work out the measurements *a*, *b* and *c* on the shapes.

(Not to scale)

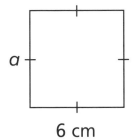

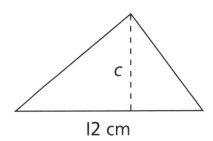

a = ☐

b = ☐

c = ☐

3 What is the area of the shaded part of each diagram?

a)

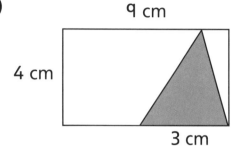

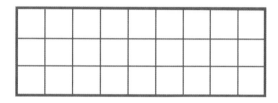

Area = ☐ cm²

b)

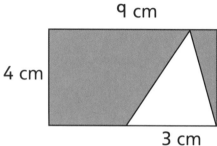

Area = ☐ cm²

4 The area of the triangle and the area of the parallelogram below are equal. If the area of the whole shape is 60 cm², what is the length of the base of the parallelogram?

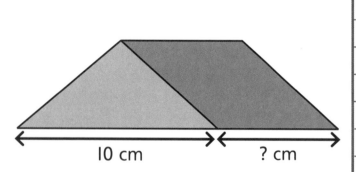

10 cm   ? cm

The length of the base of the parallelogram = ☐ cm.

5 Twelve identical rectangles are arranged to make a square frame. Calculate the area of one of the rectangles.

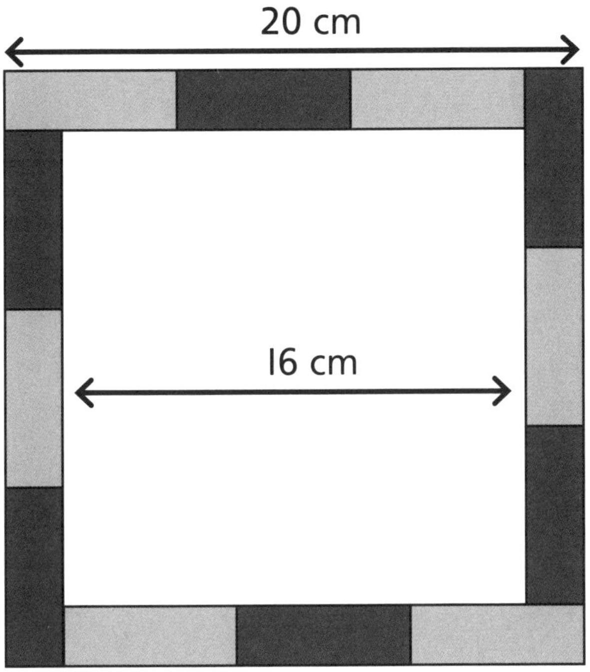

CHALLENGE

20 cm

16 cm

I think I need to find the area of the big square first.

Area = ⬜ cm²

Reflect

Write down three facts you have learnt about area in the last few lessons.

_____

_____

_____

Date: _____

Problem solving – perimeter

1. Lucy is competing in two running races. Using the information below, work out which race is longer.

Race 1

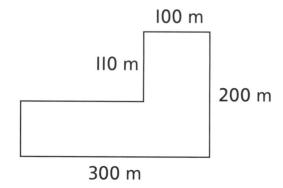

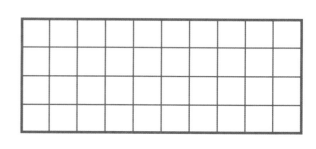

Race 2

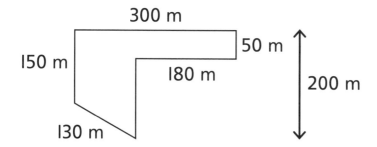

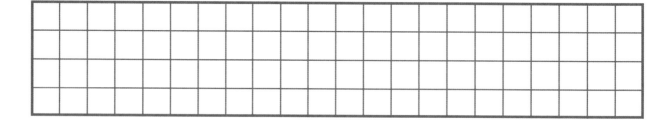

2. Ebo joins squares to make a shape with an area of 63 cm².
   Find the perimeter of the shape.

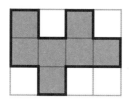

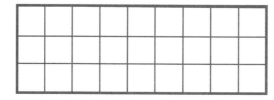

Perimeter = ☐ cm

3 A rectangle has an area of 60 cm². Its length is 11 cm more than its width. What is the perimeter of the rectangle?

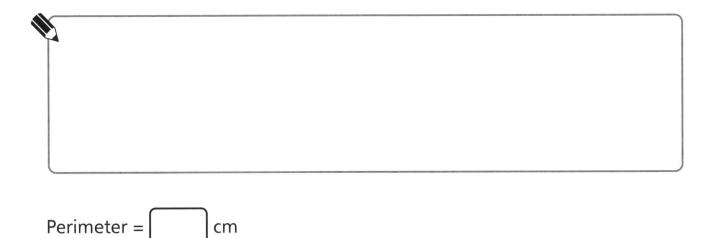

Perimeter = ☐ cm

4 These are the plans for two areas in a park. Which area has the longer perimeter?

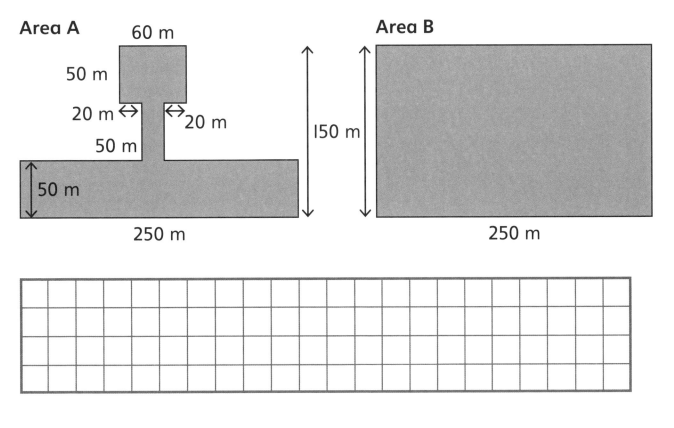

Area ☐ has the longer perimeter.

5 Zac has 8 triangular pieces of card.

He puts his pieces together to make two shapes and says that the perimeters of both shapes are equal. Is he correct? Explain your answer.

CHALLENGE

A

B

10 cm

8 cm

6 cm

_____

_____

Reflect

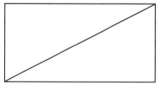

Complete this sentence.

When I cut a rectangular piece of paper into two equal parts, the

perimeters of the new shapes _____

_____.

Volume – count cubes

1 Each small cube has a volume of I cm³.

Find the number of cubes and the volume of each solid.

a)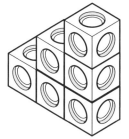

There are [ ] I cm³ cubes in the solid.

Volume = [ ] cm³

b)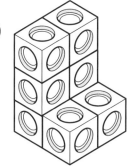

There are [ ] I cm³ cubes in the solid.

Volume = [ ] cm³

c)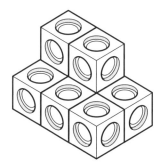

There are [ ] I cm³ cubes in the solid.

Volume = [ ] cm³

2 Circle the shapes that have a volume of 10 cm³.

A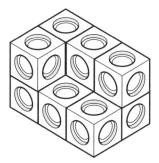

B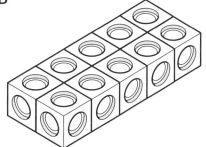

C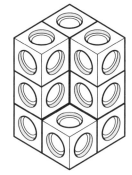

3 Match the 3D shapes that have the same volume.

A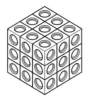

I

B

2

C

3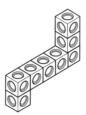

D

4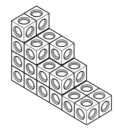

4 Lee says the volume of this solid is 6 cm³.

What mistake has Lee made?

_____

_____

5 Work out the volume of each of the following cuboids.

a)

Volume = 5 × ⬚ × ⬚

= ⬚ × ⬚

= ⬚ cm³

b)

Volume = ⬚ × ⬚ × ⬚

= ⬚ × ⬚

= ⬚ cm³

6 Ella thinks she can make a cube using all these I cm³ blocks.

Is Ella correct? Explain your answer.

_____

_____

7 Filip wants to work out the volume of two objects in the classroom.

5 cm   5 cm

He says the volume of the cylinder is 20 cm³. Is Filip correct? Explain your answer.

_____

_____

CHALLENGE

Reflect

Can you make a cube using exactly 27 smaller cubes? How do you know?

_____

_____

_____

_____

Date: _____

Volume of a cuboid

1 Find the volume of each of these cuboids.

a)

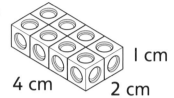

4 cm   2 cm   1 cm

Volume = 4 × 2 × 1

= ☐ cm³

b)

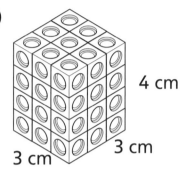

3 cm   3 cm   4 cm

Volume = ☐ × ☐ × ☐

= ☐ cm³

c)

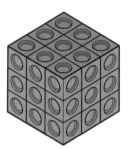

Volume = ☐ × ☐ × ☐

= ☐ cm³

d)

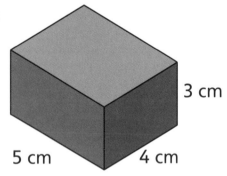

5 cm   4 cm   3 cm

Volume = ☐ × ☐ × ☐

= ☐ cm³

2 Explain two ways you can work out the volume of an 8 × 7 × 5 cuboid.

_____

_____

_____

3 A sculptor carves a hole that is 10 cm long by 11 cm wide by 4 cm deep.

He fills the hole with coloured glass.

What is the volume of the coloured glass?

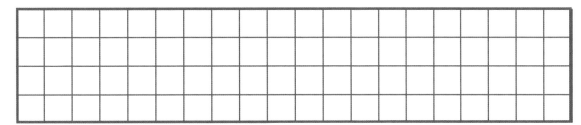

4 **a)** How wide is the piece of wood?

Volume = 480 cm^3

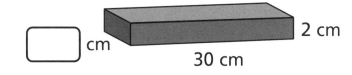

2 cm

30 cm

☐ cm

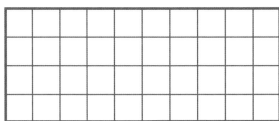

b) How long is the box?

Volume = 480 cm^3

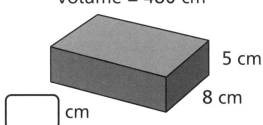

5 cm

8 cm

☐ cm

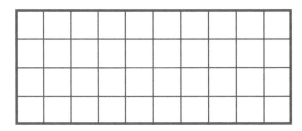

5 This cuboid has a volume of 100 cm³.

What is the height of the cuboid?

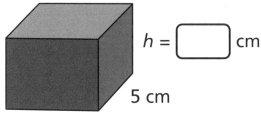

$h =$ ☐ cm

5 cm

5 cm

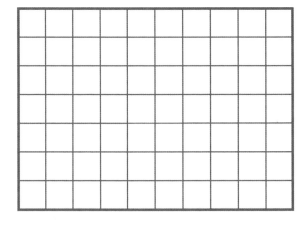

6 A cuboid has a volume of 80 m³. The length is greater than the height, which is greater than the width. Sketch two possible 3D shapes and label the dimensions.

7 A packet of tissues has the shape of a cuboid and measures 3 cm by 2 cm by 6 cm. Packets of tissues are placed in a cube-shaped cardboard box with sides of 12 cm in length.

CHALLENGE

How many packets fit into the box?

Tissues

Reflect

Explain how to find the volume of this cuboid.

3 cm
3 cm
4 cm
1 cm

End of unit check

My journal

1. Explain how you would find the area of each shape.

   a) I know that the area of this parallelogram

      is _____ because _____

      _____ .

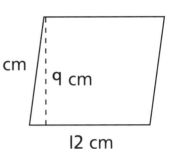

   b) I know that the area of this triangle

      is _____ because _____

      _____ .

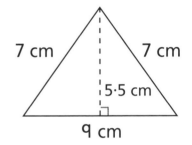

2. Rectangles with the same area have the same perimeter. True or False?
   Draw and label examples to explain your answer.

   _____

   _____

3 Look carefully at the following shapes.

A

2 cm

C

1·5 cm

8 cm

B

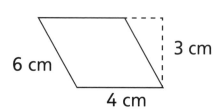

6 cm

3 cm

4 cm

D

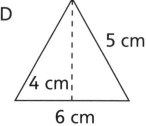

5 cm

4 cm

6 cm

a) Which shape is the odd one out?

Shape _____ is the odd one out.

b) Explain your answer.

_____

_____

c) Look at the shapes again. Find another shape that is the odd one out and give a different reason.

_____

_____

_____

Power check

How do you feel about your work in this unit?

Power puzzle

Show your working for each of these puzzles.

1 A tank measuring 8 cm by 4 cm by 6 cm is $\frac{1}{3}$ filled with water. Amy pours the water into another tank in the shape of a cube with sides 4 cm long. Can she fill the second tank?

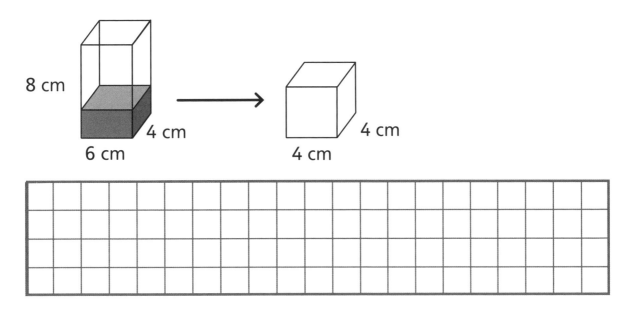

2 Isla puts a cube into a tub of water as shown in the diagram. The water rises to double the height that it was before. What are the dimensions of the cube?

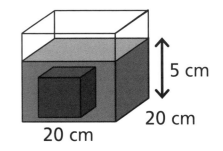

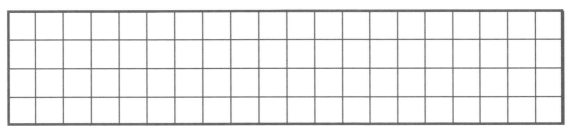

[ ] cm   ×   [ ] cm   ×   [ ] cm

161

My power points

Put a tick against the topics you have learnt about. Show how confident you are with each one by giving it a number on a scale of 1 to 3.

1 = not at all confident;
2 = getting there;
3 = very confident

Unit 7
I have learnt how to …

☐ Calculate ratios ☐

☐ Use ratios to work out amounts ☐

☐ Enlarge shapes by a scale factor ☐

☐ Identify similar shapes ☐

☐ Solve problems involving ratio ☐

Unit 8
I have learnt how to …

☐ Find and write rules ☐

☐ Write algebraic expressions ☐

☐ Make substitutions in equations ☐

☐ Write formulae ☐

☐ Write and solve equations ☐

☐ Solve equations that have multiple solutions ☐

Unit 9

I have learnt how to …

- ☐ Recognise the value of each digit in a decimal number ☐
- ☐ Multiply and divide decimals by 10, 100 and 1,000 ☐
- ☐ Convert between fractions and decimals ☐
- ☐ Multiply and divide decimals by single-digit numbers ☐

Unit 10

I have learnt how to …

- ☐ Understand percentages as parts of 100 ☐
- ☐ Find equivalent fractions, decimals and percentages ☐
- ☐ Use a range of methods to work out percentages ☐
- ☐ Find 1% and multiples of 1% ☐
- ☐ Work out missing values ☐
- ☐ Convert, order and solve problems involving fractions, percentages and decimals ☐

Unit 11

I have learnt how to …

- ☐ Find and draw shapes with the same area or perimeter ☐
- ☐ Understand how the perimeter changes when the area changes and vice versa ☐
- ☐ Calculate the area of parallelograms and triangles ☐
- ☐ Calculate and estimate the volume of cubes and cuboids ☐

Keep up the good work!

Notes

Notes

Squared paper

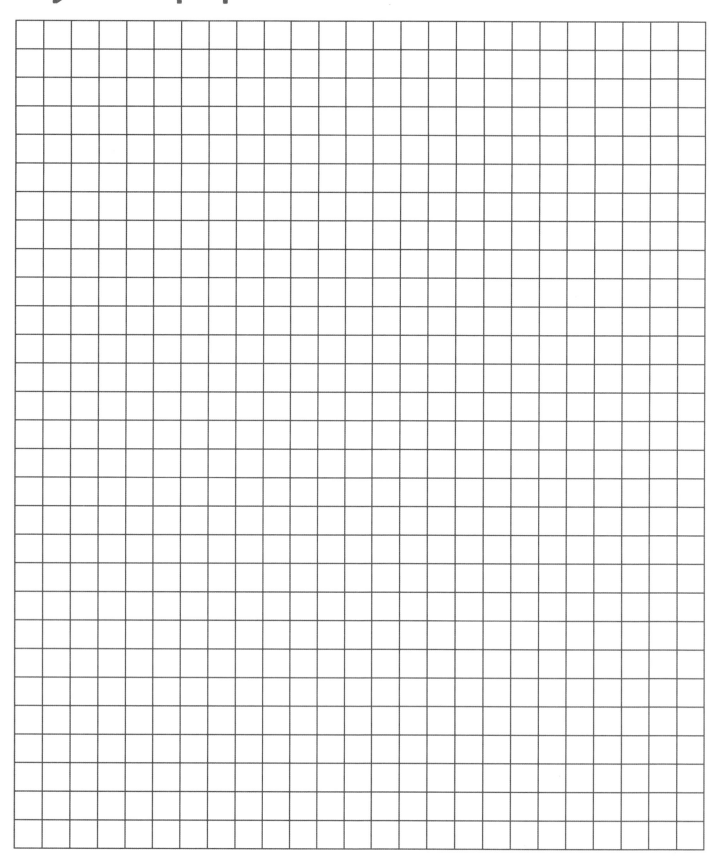

Squared paper

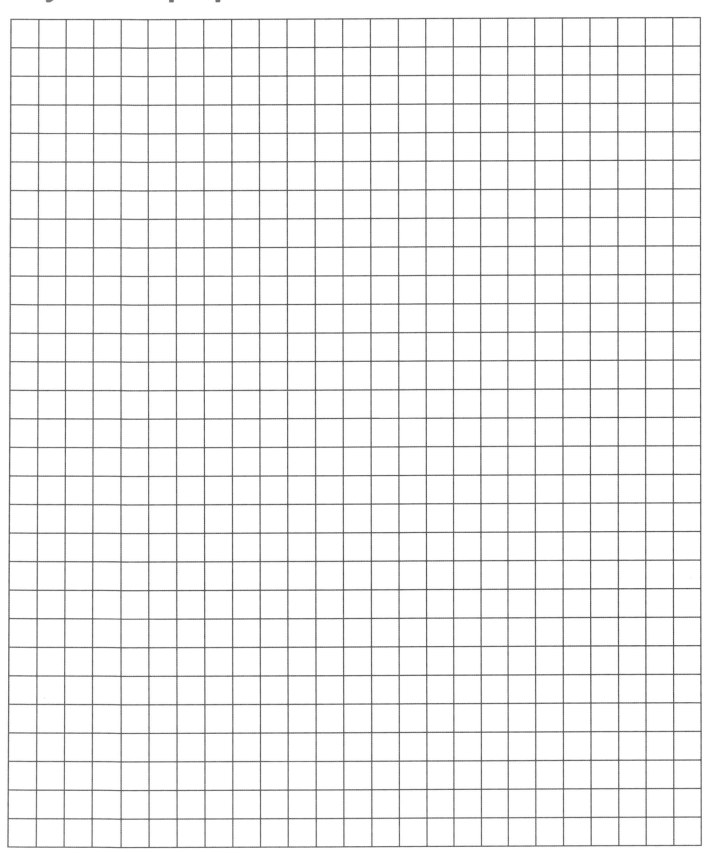

Published by Pearson Education Limited, 80 Strand, London, WC2R 0RL.

www.pearsonschools.co.uk

Text © Pearson Education Limited 2018, 2022
Edited by Pearson and Florence Production Ltd
First edition edited by Pearson, Little Grey Cells Publishing Services and Haremi Ltd
Designed and typeset by Pearson, Florence Production Ltd and PDQ Digital Media Solutions Ltd
First edition designed and typeset by Kamae Design
Original illustrations © Pearson Education Limited 2018, 2022
Illustrated by John Batten, Diego Diaz, Adam Linley and Nadene Naude at Beehive Illustration, Kamae Design,
Florence Production Ltd, and PDQ Digital Media Solutions Ltd
Images: The Royal Mint, 1990: 44
Cover design by Pearson Education Ltd
Front and back cover illustrations by Diego Diaz and Nadene Naude at Beehive Illustration

Series Editor: Tony Staneff
Lead author: Josh Lury
Consultants (first edition): Professor Liu Jian and Professor Zhang Dan

The rights of Tony Staneff and Josh Lury to be identified as authors of this work have been asserted by them in
accordance with the Copyright, Designs and Patents Act 1988.

First published 2018
This edition first published 2022

26 25 24 23
10 9 8 7 6 5 4 3

British Library Cataloguing in Publication Data
A catalogue record for this book is available from the British Library

ISBN 978 1 292 41965 7

Printed in the UK by Bell & Bain Ltd, Glasgow

For Power Maths resources go to
www.activelearnprimary.co.uk

Note from the publisher
Pearson has robust editorial processes, including answer and fact checks, to ensure the accuracy of the content in this
publication, and every effort is made to ensure this publication is free of errors. We are, however, only human, and
occasionally errors do occur. Pearson is not liable for any misunderstandings that arise as a result of errors in this
publication, but it is our priority to ensure that the content is accurate. If you spot an error, please do contact us at
resourcescorrections@pearson.com so we can make sure it is corrected.